THE OFFICIAL
NORWICH CITY
FOOTBALL CLUB
QUIZ BOOK

THE OFFICIAL NORWICH CITY FOOTBALL CLUB QUIZ BOOK

COMPILED BY
CHRIS COWLIN

APEX PUBLISHING LTD

First published in 2006 by
Apex Publishing Ltd
PO Box 7086, Clacton on Sea, Essex, CO15 5WN, England

www.apexpublishing.co.uk

British Library Cataloguing-in-Publication Data
A catalogue record for this book
is available from the British Library

ISBN 1-904444-80-6
978-1-904444-80-0

Typeset in 10.5pt Chianti BdIt Win95BT

Cover Design: Andrew Macey

Printed and bound in Great Britain

The pictures used in this book were supplied by Norwich City Football Club

This is an official product of Norwich City Football Club

Author's Note:
Please can you contact me: ChrisCowlin@btconnect.com if you find any mistakes/errors in this book as I would like to put them right on any future reprints of this book. I would also like to hear from any Norwich City fans who have enjoyed the test!

This book is dedicated to:
my son, Harry
- a future football fanatic!

FOREWORD

I must say what a privilege it is to be asked to provide the foreword for this official Norwich City quiz book and it is a pleasure to accept.

I joined Norwich City Football Club in October 1986 in a £100,000 transfer from Aberdeen FC. At the time Aberdeen were the top team in Scotland and regulars in European competitions. I never expected that my time at Norwich would coincide with some great times in the history of the Football Club.

At the end of the 1986/87 season we finished 5th in the First Division, at that time the highest position that the Club had finished in top-level football. Unfortunately we missed out on a UEFA Cup place due to English clubs being banned from European competition after the Heysel disaster. In 1988/89 we finished 4th in the First Division and had a great run in the FA Cup, only being beaten by a single goal in the semi-final at Villa Park. Once again we missed out on a UEFA Cup spot.

However in 1993/94 season we finally qualified for the UEFA Cup place through our highest ever finish in the inaugural 1992/93 FA Premier League when we finished 3rd after giving Manchester United and Aston Villa a good run for their money right up until the final few games of the season. It was a tremendous period in the Club's history travelling to the likes of Vitesse Arnhem, Bayern Munich and Inter Milan, who finally knocked us of the competition 0-2 on aggregate.

I have been lucky to have been part of a great era in the Club history but I have also found it a privilege to have been involved in many events that the Norwich City Football Club Historical

Trust arrange annually. The return of the famous 1958/59 FA Cup team who got through to the latter stages of the competition, the 1971/72 promotion-winning side, the 1985 Milk Cup winning and more recently the 10th anniversary of our 1993 UEFA Cup team have all been tremendous occasions for the fans and the players themselves.

The Historical Trust has also celebrated the Club's great history by playing games against Harwich & Parkeston in 2002 - 100 years after our first ever competitive fixture against them. In 2006 we had a fixture against our local rivals, Ipswich Town, as part of the Trust's great work.

Hopefully I have given you some good information in this foreword which will help in your enjoyment of this book. This book is a must for all Norwich City fans (young and old), it will test your knowledge of Norwich City players, past and present and the history of this great club.

I would like to take this opportunity to thank everyone at the Football Club especially the supporters for my enjoyable 12 years as a player, 7 years as Sponsorship Manager and more recently my new role as the Club's Community Ambassador.

I hope that you have great fun with this book.

Bryan Gunn

INTRODUCTION

I would first of all like to thank Bryan Gunn for writing the foreword to this book, I am very grateful for his help on this project as he is such a legend and a big part of the Norwich City history.

I would also like to thank the following people for their comments and support for this book: Jeremy Goss, Steve Bruce, Chris Woods, Delia Smith, Craig Fleming, Darren Huckerby, Doug Livermore, John Deehan, Mark Bowen, Neil Adams, Sandy Kennon, Steve Walford and Terry Allcock. There are many others but I cannot mention them all as I would take up a few pages!

I would personally like to thank Peter Rogers and Will Hoy at Norwich City Football Club, they have been a great help to me during the production of this book. Thanks also to Mavis Thurston at Norwich City Football Club. I would also like to thank Gus Honeywood for his help, he runs **www.forces2canaries.co.uk** - well worth a visit!

I am honoured to donate £1 from each book sale to 'The Norwich City Football Club Historical Trust'. The Trust seeks to build and preserve a collection of material to stimulate interest in the Club's history and is in the process of setting up a museum at the club - I am sure all fans will enjoy that!

I hope you enjoy this book, it was a true pleasure compiling it as I learnt so much about this great club and the past players - I hope it brings back some wonderful memories of the Canaries victories and the various matches at Carrow Road.

In closing, I would like to thank all my friends and family for encouraging me to complete this book.

Best wishes, Chris Cowlin

HISTORY OF THE CLUB

1. Norwich City were formed in 1902, but what year did they turn professional - 1903, 1904 or 1905?

2. What is the club's nickname?

3. In March 1963, Norwich recorded their record attendance of 43,984 at home in the FA Cup, against which team - Leeds United, Ipswich Town or Leicester City?

4. Which player won 35 caps for Wales, a club record, whilst a Norwich player?

5. In January 2005, Norwich paid £3 million for Dean Ashton (a record for the club). Which club did he sign from - Chesterfield, Crewe Alexandra or Chelsea?

6. Norwich City's record goalscorer in a season was Ralph Hunt during 1955/1956. How many goals did he score?

7. Which player holds the record for making the most league appearances for Norwich, making 590 between 1946 and 1964 - Martin Peters, Ron Ashman or Bryan Gunn?

8. In what year did Norwich first play in European competition?

9. Which manager was Norwich's first in their professional history - John Bond, Mike Walker or John Bowman?

10. In 1930, Norwich recorded their biggest ever league win in Division 3 South, against which team, beating them 10-2?

BRYAN GUNN

11. In which year was Bryan born - 1961, 1962 or 1963?

12. How many first-team games did Bryan play for the Canaries?

13. How many Scotland caps did Bryan win for his country - 4, 6 or 8?

14. Against which county did Bryan make his international debut in a 3-1 defeat at Pittodrie Stadium in 1990?

15. From which Scottish club did Norwich sign Bryan in 1986?

16. Against which club did Bryan make his Canaries league debut in November 1986 in a 2-1 home win - West Ham United, Arsenal or Tottenham Hotspur?

17. Which Norwich manager bought Bryan for the Canaries and gave him his debut?

18. How many times did Bryan win Norwich 'Player of the Season' - 1, 2 or 3?

19. When Bryan left Carrow Road, which Scottish team did he sign for - Motherwell, Hibernian or Hearts?

20. Which Scottish manager gave Bryan his Scottish debut?

1986/1987

21. Who was Norwich's top league goalscorer with 16 league goals in 42 appearances?

22. Can you name the two goalkeepers that played for the Canaries during the season?

23. Which London club did Norwich beat 4-1 in the League Cup 3rd round with Kevin Drinkell and David Hodgson (3) scoring?

24. What position in the league did Norwich finish in Division One?

25. Steve Bruce scored three league goals during the season, against which sides?

26. Norwich recorded their biggest win of the season in September, winning 4-1, against which club?

27. Who was Canaries' captain during the season?

28. How many of their 42 league games did Norwich win?

29. Against which London side did Norwich play on the opening day of the league season, drawing 0-0?

30. Norwich beat Arsenal 2-1 at Highbury on the last day of the season, but which two players scored the goals?

NATIONALITIES

Match up the player with his nationality

31.	Dickson Etuhu	Irish
32.	Robert Green	Irish
33.	Mark Bowen	Scottish
34.	Jurgen Colin	Welsh
35.	Alan Black	English
36.	Mal Lucas	English
37.	Chris Sutton	Dutch
38.	Bobby Brennan	English
39.	Darren Huckerby	Nigerian
40.	Michael Spillane	Welsh

MARK BOWEN

41.   In what year was Mark born - 1959, 1963 or 1967?

42.   Mark joined Norwich in July 1987, from which club?

43.   Which manager signed Mark for Norwich?

44.   In what position did Mark play for Norwich (most often)?

45.   Mark made 320 league appearances for Norwich, scoring how many goals?

46.   In what season did Mark win Norwich 'Player of the Season'?

47.   What country did Mark represent at full international level, winning 35 caps?

48.   In 2001, Mark was appointed assistant manager to which former Norwich player at Birmingham City?

49.   Mark scored in the UEFA Cup match at the Olympic Stadium, Munich, in 1993 against Bayern Munich, but what was the score in the game?

50.   Mark left Carrow Road in July 1996 and signed for which team on a free transfer?

2005/2006

51. The first league win came with Matthias Doumbe (own goal) and Dean Ashton scoring, against which club?

52. Norwich drew in the first three league games, but what was the identical score - 0-0, 1-1 or 2-2?

53. Norwich beat Brighton & Hove Albion 3-0 in February 2006, but who scored the goals?

54. In what league position did Norwich finish - 7th, 8th or 9th?

55. Which player scored a hat-trick against Southampton at Carrow Road in the 3-1 home win?

56. Which team did Norwich beat 3-1 away on Boxing Day 2005?

57. Which team did Norwich beat 1-0 away in the League Cup 1st round, with Leon McKenzie scoring?

58. Who was Norwich manager during this season?

59. In April 2006, which two players scored in the 2-1 home win against Leicester City?

60. In April 2006, which Welsh striker scored against a former side in a 1-0 away win?

JOHN DEEHAN

61.   In what year was John born - 1956, 1957 or 1958?

62.   John finished top league goalscorer during 1983/1984 with how many goals - 10, 15 or 20?

63.   In September 1984, John scored a hat-trick in a 3-2 home win, against which team?

64.   Which medal did John win whilst at Norwich during March 1985?

65.   John made 162 league appearances for the Canaries, scoring how many goals?

66.   In what position did John play for Norwich - defender, midfielder or centre forward?

67.   Which two Midlands teams did John play for before joining Norwich City?

68.   John scored on his league debut for Norwich in 1981 in a 3-1 home defeat, against which team?

69.   Against which London club did John score his first Norwich hat-trick in 1982?

70.   Which team did John sign for when he left Norwich in 1986?

UEFA CUP - 1993/1994

71. Can you name the Dutch side that Norwich played against in the 1st round?

72. Following on from the previous question, which players scored the goals in the 3-0 home win?

73. Which two players scored in the famous 2-1 away win at Bayern Munich in the 2nd round?

74. Can you name seven of the starting eleven who beat Bayern Munich in Germany?

75. Which goalkeeper played in all six UEFA Cup games?

76. Norwich drew 1-1 in their 2nd round, 2nd leg tie with Bayern Munich, but who scored for Norwich?

77. Which player scored three goals in his six UEFA Cup appearances?

78. Who was the Norwich manager during this season?

79. How many goals did Norwich score in their six matches?

80. Which team knocked Norwich out of the competition in the 3rd round?

LEAGUE APPEARANCES - 1

Match up the player with the number of league appearances he made

81.	Terry Allcock	93
82.	Roy McCrohan	378
83.	Peter Grant	200 (3)
84.	Tony Cottee	334 (5)
85.	Ken Nethercott	315 (5)
86.	Bobby Brennan	314 (27)
87.	Steve Walford	5 (2)
88.	Mark Bowen	64 (4)
89.	Colin Suggett	385
90.	Ian Crook	225

WHERE DID THEY GO? - 1

Match up the player with the club he moved to from Norwich

91.   John Polston   Stoke City

92.   Matt Jackson   Southend United

93.   Chris Sutton   Wycombe Wanderers

94.   Jim Brennan   Middlesbrough

95.   Darel Russell   Blackburn Rovers

96.   Viv Busby   Reading

97.   Rob Newman   Wigan Athletic

98.   Keith O'Neill   Southampton

99.   Paul Dalglish   Stoke City

100. Clint Easton   Wigan Athletic

CHRIS WOODS

101. In what year was Chris born - 1957, 1958 or 1959?

102. From which London club did Norwich sign Chris in 1981?

103. Following on from the previous question, how much did he cost Norwich?

104. In 1981, Chris made his debut in a 3-0 defeat, against which club?

105. For which country did Chris win full international caps during his playing career?

106. In which season did Chris win Norwich 'Player of the Season'?

107. How many league appearances did Chris make for Norwich - 116, 216 or 316?

108. Which Norwich manager handed Chris his debut for the Canaries?

109. How many full international caps did Chris win for his country?

110. In 1998, which top-flight team did Chris join as goalkeeping coach?

NORWICH CITY V. IPSWICH TOWN

111. Which player scored a hat-trick in the League Cup in a 4-2 win against Ipswich in September 1968?

112. In March 2004, Norwich beat Ipswich 3-1 at Carrow Road, with Darren Huckerby scoring, but which defender scored two goals in the game?

113. Who scored the only goal when the sides met in Division One in December 1977 in a 1-0 home win?

114. August 1972 saw Norwich's first-ever victory in top flight football over Town, but what was the score?

115. Which two players scored in the 3-1 home win in October 1996 in Division One?

116. Which player scored in the 1-0 away win in September 2005?

117. In December 1974, Norwich beat Ipswich 2-1 in a League Cup 5th round replay, but which player scored both goals?

118. What was the score when the sides met in March 1995 at Carrow Road in the Premier League?

119. Norwich beat Town 1-0 in August 1993 at Carrow Road, but who scored?

120. Which striker scored both goals for Norwich at Portman Road in a 2-0 win in December 2003?

IAN BUTTERWORTH

121. In what year was Ian born in Cheshire - 1962, 1964 or 1966?

122. Ian made his Norwich league debut in September 1986 against Aston Villa, but what was the score in the game?

123. How many league goals did Ian score in his 235 appearances?

124. Ken Brown signed Ian for Norwich in 1986, from which club?

125. How many England Under-21 caps did Ian win in his career?

126. In what position did Ian play for Norwich?

127. Which three sports did Ian represent at county level?

128. Against which team did Ian score his first goal in January 1989 in a 3-2 away win?

129. Against which team did Ian score his only goal of the 1992/1993 Premier League season?

130. Of which club was Ian appointed assistant manager in 1998 and then resigned in 2000?

POSITION IN THE LEAGUE - 1

Match up the season with the position Norwich finished in the league

131.	2005/2006	12th
132.	2003/2004	14th
133.	2001/2002	9th
134.	1999/2000	1st
135.	1997/1998	10th
136.	1995/1996	6th
137.	1993/1994	16th
138.	1991/1992	15th
139.	1989/1990	18th
140.	1987/1988	12th

NORWICH CITY V. ARSENAL

141.　The sides played their first Premier League game in August 1992. Norwich were 2-0 down at half-time, but what was the final score?

142.　Which two players scored the goals in the 2-2 draw on the last day of the 1989/1990 season?

143.　On Boxing Day 1984, Norwich beat the Gunners 1-0 at Carrow Road, but who scored the goal wearing the number 10 shirt?

144.　Which player scored a League Cup hat-trick against Arsenal in November 1972?

145.　Which two players scored when Norwich beat Arsenal 2-1 on the final day of the 1986/1987 season?

146.　What was the score when the sides met at Carrow Road in Division One during February 1976 - 1-1, 2-1 or 3-1?

147.　What was the score when the sides met in April 1980 at Carrow Road?

148.　Which ex-Arsenal player, nicknamed 'Rocky', played for Norwich during 1996/1997?

149.　In which year did Norwich beat Arsenal 2-1 in the FA Cup 4th round, with Tom Johnston scoring both goals?

150.　Norwich beat the Gunners 3-1 in April 1983, but which two players scored the goals?

NORWICH IN THE LEAGUE CUP

151. Which player scored a hat-trick while captaining the side in a 5-0 3rd round replay in October 1962?

152. Can you name seven of the starting eleven that played in the 1985 Cup Final success?

153. Norwich played Spurs in the 1973 final, but which two other London teams did they play in the 5th round and semi-final?

154. Which player scored the own-goal that gave Norwich victory in the1985 final at Wembley?

155. Norwich beat Ipswich 4-2 in the 2nd round in September 1968, but who scored a hat-trick in the game?

156. Which striker scored a 3rd round replay hat-trick against Bradford City in November 1995 in a 5-3 away win?

157. Which team did Norwich play in the 1975 final at Wembley?

158. Which team knocked Norwich out in the 1973/1974 semi-finals, beating them 2-1 over the two legs?

159. In 1962, Norwich beat Rochdale in the final over two legs, but what was the aggregate score?

160. Can you name seven of the starting eleven that played in the 1975 Cup Final?

POT LUCK - 1

161. Which player scored Norwich's first ever goal in European competition?

162. In what year was Delia Smith awarded the OBE?

163. What is Norwich's nickname?

164. In which year did Norwich play in their first major Cup Final?

165. Which ex-Scottish international, who had also played for Arsenal and West Ham, was appointed manager in 1957?

166. In which colours do Norwich play?

167. During April 1974, which player became Norwich's then youngest ever player to play for the club, aged 17?

168. Which player won the Norwich City 'Player of the Season' award during 1970/1971?

169. Which player scored a record 37 goals in the 1962/1963 season?

170. In which year did Norwich first play in the UEFA Cup - 1961, 1985 or 1993?

MARTIN O'NEILL

171. In what year was Martin born - 1950, 1952 or 1954?

172. Against which team did Martin score a brace for Norwich in a 5-1 home win in September 1982?

173. In what year did Martin both become and leave as Norwich City manager?

174. As a player, in which positions did Martin play - defender/midfielder, defender/forward or midfielder/forward?

175. How many full international caps did Martin win for his country - 54, 64 or 74?

176. Which team did Martin manage between 1990 and 1995?

177. When Martin left Carrow Road as manager, what team did he go on to manage a month later?

178. What nationality is Martin?

179. What award was Martin given in 2004 for his services to sport?

180. Which Midlands side was Martin appointed manager of in August 2006?

1970s

181. Who finished as City's top league goalscorer with ten goals during 1978/1979?

182. Norwich reached the final of which two Cups in 1973?

183. Norwich beat West Ham 3-1 on the opening day of season 1977/1978, but who scored the goals?

184. Which two players scored 33 league goals between them during 1974/1975?

185. Against which team did Viv Busby score a league hat-trick on New Year's Day 1977 in a 3-2 home win?

186. Which two players both scored 15 league goals during 1970/1971?

187. Who was City's captain for 1973/1974?

188. Norwich beat Nottingham Forest 3-1 away in October 1974, but who scored a hat-trick in the game?

189. Which goalkeeper played in every single League and Cup game during 1975/1976?

190. Who finished as City's top league goalscorer with 11 goals during 1972/1973?

WHERE DID THEY GO? - 2

Match up the player with the club he moved to from Norwich

191. Daryl Sutch   Leicester City

192. Thomas Helveg   Viking Stavanger

193. Max Briggs   Bristol Rovers

194. Tony Spearing   Borussia
                                Monchengladbach

195. Robert Green   Newcastle United

196. Erik Fuglestad   Southend United

197. Jamie Cureton   Oxford United

198. Ian Davies   West Ham United

199. Dean Ashton   Fulham

200. Roger Brown   West Ham United

TIM SHERWOOD

201. In what year was Tim born - 1965, 1967 or 1969?

202. Norwich signed Tim from Watford, in what year?

203. Tim made his Norwich debut against which London side?

204. Tim Sherwood scored his first goal in a 4-4 home draw with Southampton, but which two other players scored?

205. How many full England international caps did Tim win for his country?

206. In what position did Tim play during his playing days?

207. How many league goals did Tim score during 1990/1991, finishing Norwich's joint-top goalscorer for the season with Dale Gordon?

208. How many league goals did Tim score for Norwich in his career - 5, 10 or 15?

209. Tim scored on the opening day of the 1990/1991 season in a 3-2 home win, against which team?

210. When Tim left Norwich City, what team did he sign for?

GARY MEGSON

211. In what year was Gary born - 1955, 1957 or 1959?

212. Gary signed for Norwich in 1992, from which club?

213. In what position in the Premier League did Norwich finish during Gary's first season at Carrow Road?

214. Gary took over as Norwich manager in December 1995, but in what year did he leave as manager?

215. Which manager signed Gary for Norwich?

216. As manager of which team did Gary take over in January 2005?

217. Gary made 46 league appearances for Norwich, scoring one goal, against who?

218. At which club did Gary start his career at as an apprentice before signing professional forms?

219. Which was the first team that Gary managed?

220. Which team did Gary manage between 2000 and 2004?

2004/2005

221. With which team did Norwich draw 1-1 on the opening day of the season at Carrow Road?

222. Norwich's first league victory was on 20 November 2004, winning 2-1 against which team?

223. Following on from the previous question, who scored both goals for Norwich in the game?

224. Which player scored a penalty in a 1-0 win against Birmingham City in May 2005?

225. In what position did Norwich finish during this season?

226. In January, Norwich drew 4-4 with Middlesbrough. Which four players scored for the Canaries?

227. Who was manager of the Canaries during this season?

228. In April, Norwich beat Newcastle United 2-1, with Youssef Safri and Dean Ashton scoring, but who scored the opponents' goal?

229. Which striker left Carrow Road at the end of the season and signed for Elfsborg Boras?

230. In April 2005, Norwich beat Manchester United 2-0 at Carrow Road, but which players scored the goals?

RUEL FOX

231. Where was Ruel born in 1968 - Norwich, Colchester or Ipswich?

232. Which Norwich manager gave Ruel his Norwich debut?

233. Ruel scored in Norwich's first Premier League game against Arsenal, but which two other Norwich players scored in the 4-2 win in August 1992?

234. Which squad number did Ruel wear during 1993/1994?

235. Which team did Norwich beat 4-0 in August 1993, with Ruel scoring twice?

236. Which Midlands team did Ruel play for between 2000-2002 - Aston Villa, Walsall or West Bromwich Albion?

237. Ruel played in 172 league games for Norwich, scoring how many goals?

238. When Ruel left Carrow Road in February 1994, which club did he sign for?

239. Ruel scored two league goals during 1991/1992, against which two London teams?

240. Ruel scored in all of Norwich's last three league games during 1989/1990. Can you name two of the three opposing clubs?

24

NORWICH & IPSWICH CONNECTIONS

241. Which goalkeeper left Carrow in 2001 and joined Ipswich?

242. Who played for Norwich between 1955 and 1957 and was later Bill McGarry's assistant manager for Ipswich?

243. Who played for Norwich between 1982 and 1985 and Ipswich between 1989 and 1990?

244. Who played for Norwich during 1980/1981 and managed Ipswich Town late in his management career?

245. Which player moved direct from Carrow Road to Portman Road in 1986?

246. Which goalkeeper played for Norwich, making his debut in 1978, and later played for Town in the Premier League?

247. Which ex-Norwich coach joined the Ipswich coaching staff in the summer of 2006?

248. Which centre forward played for Norwich during the early 1980s and for Ipswich in the seventies?

249. Which midfielder moved directly from Portman Road to Carrow Road in 1986?

250. Who made eleven league appearances for Norwich and was later Joe Royle's assistant at Portman Road?

JEREMY GOSS

251.   In which year was Jeremy born - 1961, 1963 or 1965?

252.   Jeremy scored two league goals during 1994/1995, against which teams?

253.   Jeremy made his Norwich first team debut in 1984 as a substitute in a 2-1 defeat, against which team?

254.   Against which London side did Jeremy score in a 4-3 away win in February 1992?

255.   What International team did Jeremy play for?

256.   In January 1993, Jeremy scored one league goal in Norwich's first premier league season in a 4-2 home win, against which side?

257.   Jeremy made 188 league appearances for Norwich, scoring how many goals?

258.   Against which two London sides did Jeremy score during 1987/1988, with Norwich winning both games?

259.   Jeremy played in all six UEFA cup games during 1993, scoring three goals against which two teams?

260.   How many league goals did Jeremy score during 1993/1994 - 0, 3 or 6?

WHO AM I?

261. Born in Ipswich, I made my Norwich debut in 1986 and played in my final game for them in 1994. I played for Newcastle and Spurs in the premier league.

262. I signed for Norwich from Queens Park Rangers and made my debut in goal in March 1981. I left Carrow Road in 1986 for Glasgow Rangers.

263. I was born in 1971, I signed from Oldham Athletic in 1997 and I had a testimonial in 2006 against Newcastle.

264. I was born in 1945, my past clubs include Southampton and Tottenham Hotspur and I scored on my Norwich debut in 1978.

265. I made my debut in August 1989, I played in midfield, and later in my career I captained Blackburn Rovers to the Premier League title.

266. I signed for Norwich from Manchester United and made my debut in August 1992, scoring two goals.

267. I was born in Nottingham in 1973, I left Carrow Road in 1994 and I played in a strike partnership with Alan Shearer.

268. I was born in Cyprus, I played for Norwich between 1984 and 1996 and I scored goals in the UEFA cup against Bayern Munich.

269. I was born in 1948, I made my debut for City in December 1982, I played as a striker and my former clubs include Manchester City and Southampton.

270. I signed for Norwich in 1994 from Oldham Athletic and I left Carrow Road and re-signed for Oldham in 1999.

JOHN POLSTON

271.   In what year was John born - 1966, 1968 or 1970?

272.   John signed for Norwich in July 1990 for £250,000, from which club?

273.   What nationality is John?

274.   John made his debut against Sunderland in August 1990, but what was the score in the game?

275.   Which squad number did John wear during the Premier League season 1994/1995?

276.   How many league appearances did John make for Norwich - 115, 215 or 315?

277.   In February 1992, John scored in a 4-3 away win, against which side?

278.   John made 27 league appearances in his first season at Carrow Road, scoring how many goals - 4, 5 or 6?

279.   Against which team did John score in the League Cup 3rd round and 3rd round replay in October/November 1994?

280.   Which club did John join when he left Norwich?

CHRIS SUTTON

281.   In what year was Chris born in Nottingham?

282.   Chris made his Norwich debut in May 1991 in a 1-0 win against which club?

283.   In what season did Chris win Norwich 'Player of the Year'?

284.   Chris won one England cap in November 1997, against which country?

285.   When Chris left Carrow Road in 1994, which team did he sign for, costing £5 million?

286.   Following on from the previous question, which trophy did he win in his first season with his new club?

287.   Chris made 126 appearances for Norwich, scoring how many goals (in all competitions)?

288.   Chris scored a hat-trick against which side in a 4-2 home win in April 1993?

289.   Which Scottish team did Chris play for between 2000 and 2006?

290.   How many league goals did Chris score in his final season at Carrow Road?

1992/1993 - THE FIRST PREMIER LEAGUE SEASON

291. Norwich finished 3rd in the league. Name the two sides that finished above them.

292. Who was manager of the Canaries?

293. Against which team did Norwich play their first Premier League game, winning 4-2?

294. What was the score in the first Premier League match against Ipswich Town?

295. Can you name the three players who played in every Premier League game?

296. Which Canaries striker finished as Norwich's top goalscorer with 15 goals?

297. Against which team did Chris Sutton score a hat-trick in April in a 4-2 win?

298. Which player scored a brace against Middlesbrough on the last day of the season?

299. John Polston scored his only goal of the season in a 1-0 home win against which side?

300. Can you name the three players that scored the goals in the 3-0 away win against Nottingham Forest?

NORWICH LEAGUE
CUP WINNERS - 1985

301. Who did Norwich beat in the final?

302. What was the score in the game?

303. Which team did Norwich beat in the semi-final?

304. Norwich beat Grimsby Town 1-0 in the 5th round, but who scored the goal?

305. Which manager led Norwich to their success?

306. Who was the Norwich captain during this success?

307. Which player scored five goals in the competition in his nine appearances?

308. Which Lancashire side did Norwich play in the 2nd round?

309. Where was the Cup final played?

310. John Deehan, Steve Bruce and which other player played in all nine League Cup games duing this success?

ROB NEWMAN

311. In what year was Rob born?

312. Which manager signed Rob for Norwich?

313. Rob made his Norwich debut in August 1991 in a 2-2 draw, against which club?

314. In what position did Rob mostly play during his playing career at Norwich City?

315. In September 1994, Rob scored at Portman Road in a 2-1 win, but which other Norwich player scored?

316. During the summer of 1991, Rob signed for the Canaries for £600,000 from which club?

317. To which two clubs did Rob go on loan during 1997/1998?

318. Rob left Carrow Road at the end of the 1997/1998 season to join which Essex side?

319. Rob scored two goals in Norwich's Premier League season (1992/1993) against which teams?

320. How many league goals did Rob score for Norwich in his career - 4, 14 or 24?

IAN CROOK

321. Ian scored in a 2-1 away win in December 1987, with Dale Gordon also scoring, against which team?

322. Ian made his league debut in August 1986 in a 0-0 draw, against which club?

323. Ian scored his first goal for Norwich in November 1986 in a 2-1 home win, against which team?

324. Which country did Ian represent at 'B' level?

325. Ian made 341 league appearances for Norwich, scoring how many goals?

326. Ken Brown signed Ian for Norwich during 1986, from which club?

327. In what position did Ian play during his Norwich career?

328. Ian scored five league goals in his first season at Carrow Road. Against which team did he score on the last day of the season, winning 2-1?

329. Ian scored against which league club both at home and away during 1990/1991?

330. In which competition did Ian score for Norwich during 1994/1995 against Grimsby Town?

MIKE MILLIGAN

331. In what year was Mike born in Manchester - 1965, 1967 or 1969?

332. Mike made his debut in a 2-1 win against which team, with Carl Bradshaw and Rob Newman scoring in the game?

333. Which Norwich manager signed Mike in 1994?

334. In what position did Mike play for Norwich?

335. Mike scored two goals in his first season at Carrow Road, against which clubs?

336. Mike made 124 league appearances for Norwich, scoring how many goals?

337. Against which London team did Mike score during November 1996?

338. Where did Norwich finish in the Premier League in Mike's season, 1994/1995 - 16th, 18th or 20th?

339. Against which two teams did Mike score during 1995/1996?

340. Mike left Carrow Road in 2000 on a free transfer, but which team did he join?

DIVISION 1 CHAMPIONS
- 2003/2004

341. In April, Norwich beat Burnley 5-3 away. Can you name the three strikers that scored the goals between them?

342. In December, Norwich beat which Welsh-based team 4-1 at Carrow Road?

343. Against which team did Norwich draw 4-4 away during January 2004?

344. How many of their 46 league games did Norwich win - 20, 24 or 28?

345. Which manager guided Norwich to this success?

346. Which team did Norwich beat 1-0 at Carrow Road in October, with Damien Francis scoring?

347. How many points did Norwich finish with after their 46 league games - 88, 94 or 100?

348. In December 2003, which four players scored in a 4-0 away win against Derby City?

349. Against which team did Norwich play their final home game, beating them 3-2?

350. Which team did Norwich beat 3-1 on the last day of the season, with Craig Fleming and Iwan Roberts (2) scoring?

ROBERT FLECK

351. Where was Robert born in 1965 - Edinburgh, Dundee or Glasgow?

352. From which club did Norwich sign Robert in 1987?

353. How many league goals did Robert score for Norwich during 1995/1996?

354. Which team did Robert play for between 1992 and 1995 before returning to Carrow Road?

355. In which season did Robert win Norwich's 'Player of the Year'?

356. Against which team did Robert make his debut for Norwich in December 1987 in a 1-0 defeat?

357. How many league goals did Robert score in his Norwich career?

358. Robert scored two goals during the 1997/1998 season, against which two clubs?

359. How many league goals did Robert score for Norwich during 1988/1989 - 8, 10 or 12?

360. Robert scored an FA Cup hat-trick in a 8-0 win in January 1989, against which club?

PLAYER OF THE SEASON

Match the player with the season in which he won the award

361.	2005/2006	Andy Marshall
362.	2003/2004	Ian Culverhouse
363.	2000/2001	Kevin Keelan
364.	1998/1999	Gary Doherty
365.	1994/1995	Iwan Roberts
366.	1990/1991	Martin Peters
367.	1987/1988	Jon Newsome
368.	1984/1985	Craig Fleming
369.	1976/1977	Steve Bruce
370.	1973/1974	Bryan Gunn

STEVE BRUCE

371. In what year was Steve born - 1958, 1960 or 1962?

372. Steve made his Norwich league debut in August 1984 in a 3-3 draw at Carrow Road, against which team?

373. How many league goals did Steve score in his 141 appearances?

374. From which team did Ken Brown sign Steve in 1984?

375. During 1984/1985, which award did Steve win whilst at Carrow Road?

376. During what season did Steve captain the team, taking over from Dave Watson?

377. How many goals did Steve score during the 1985/1986 Division 2 Championship season - 4, 8 or 12?

378. Steve scored two goals for Norwich during 1987/1988, against which two sides?

379. At which team was Steve appointed as manager in 2001?

380. Steve left Carrow Road in December 1987 and signed for which team?

POSITION IN THE LEAGUE - 2

Match up the season with the position Norwich finished in the league

381.	1985/1986	10th
382.	1983/1984	13th
383.	1981/1982	1st
384.	1979/1980	9th
385.	1977/1978	1st
386.	1975/1976	12th
387.	1973/1974	14th
388.	1971/1972	11th
389.	1969/1970	22nd
390.	1967/1968	3rd

DALE GORDON

391. In what year was Dale born in Norfolk - 1963, 1965 or 1967?

392. Dale made his Norwich league debut against which team in a 3-3 home draw?

393. In what year did Dale make his Norwich debut?

394. In which season did Dale win 'Player of the Season'?

395. During April 1986, Dale scored one league goal in 1-1 draw in the Division 2 Championship season, against which side?

396. How many goals did Dale score in his 206 league appearances for Norwich?

397. Against which club did Dale score his first Norwich goal in a 3-0 home win?

398. Against which three teams did Dale score in the league during 1989/1990?

399. Dale left Carrow Road in November 1991, joining which Scottish team?

400. For which team did Dale score to make it their first Premier League goal in history in 1993?

TED MACDOUGALL

401. Ted was born in Inverness in what year?

402. From which London side did Norwich sign Ted?

403. Which Norwich manager signed Ted for the Canaries?

404. Ted made 112 league appearances, scoring how many goals?

405. For which country did Ted win full international caps whilst at Norwich City?

406. Ted scored a league hat-trick in August 1975, winning 5-3 at Carrow Road, against which club?

407. In what position did Ted play in his Norwich career?

408. Ted played all 42 league matches during 1975/1976, scoring how many goals?

409. Against which team did Ted score both goals in a 2-0 win in September 1974?

410. In December 1973, Ted made his Norwich debut against which team?

HONOURS

Match the success with the year it was achieved

411.	FA Youth Cup winners	1973
412.	Division One champions	1985
413.	FA Cup semi-finalists	1975
414.	Division Two champions	2004
415.	League Cup winners	1983
416.	League Cup runners-up	1962
417.	Division Two champions	1992
418.	League Cup winners	1934
419.	Division Three (South) champions	1986
420.	League Cup runners-up	1972

MARTIN PETERS

421. Martin made 207 league appearances for Norwich, but how many goals did he score?

422. Where was Martin born - Manchester, Oxford or London?

423. Against which club did Martin make his debut in March 1975, drawing 0-0 away?

424. Which manager signed Martin for Norwich in 1975?

425. Following on from the previous question, which club did he sign from?

426. Martin scored two goals in his first season at Norwich, both in 3-0 wins, against which clubs?

427. Martin played in all 42 league games for Norwich during 1976/1977. Who was the only other player to do so?

428. In 1976, Martin was handed the Norwich captaincy, but which captain did he take over from?

429. Martin scored in the World Cup final in 1966, but which player scored a hat-trick in that game?

430. When Martin left Carrow Road in 1980, which team did he join?

SQUAD NUMBERS - 2006/2007

Match the player with his squad number for the season

431.	Robert Earnshaw	17
432.	Dion Dublin	27
433.	Adam Drury	10
434.	Andy Hughes	2
435.	Darren Huckerby	24
436.	Gary Doherty	9
437.	Dickson Etuhu	6
438.	Paul McVeigh	3
439.	Matthieu Louis-Jean	18
440.	Jurgen Colin	20

1988/1989

441.   Who was Norwich City's manager?

442.   Which two players scored in the 2-1 opening-day win
        against Nottingham Forest?

443.   Which player scored four goals for Norwich in the FA Cup
        4th round 8-0 win against Sutton United?

444.   In what position in Division One did Norwich finish?

445.   Which two 'Roberts' scored the three goals between
        them in the 3-2 away win at Middlesbrough?

446.   Who was Norwich's highest league goalscorer with ten
        goals?

447.   Who were the only two Norwich players to play and start
        in every league game?

448.   Which London side did Norwich beat 3-1 in the FA Cup
        quarter-final to reach the semi-finals against Everton?

449.   Who captained Norwich during the season?

450.   Norwich beat Liverpool 1-0 at Anfield during December,
        but which player scored the goal?

MICK CHANNON

451. In what year was Mick born in Wiltshire - 1946, 1948 or 1950?

452. How many league goals did Mick score in his 88 appearances for Norwich?

453. Mick made his Norwich debut against Ipswich Town in December 1982 at Portman Road, but what was the score?

454. Which team did Mick play for between 1977 and 1979?

455. Mick won 46 caps for England, scoring how many goals - 11, 21 or 31?

456. Can you name the three sides that Mick scored against in the League Cup, on the way to their 1985 success?

457. In what position did Mick play for Norwich?

458. Which manager signed Mick for Norwich in 1982?

459. Mick scored a League Cup hat-trick in a 3-0 home win in October 1983, against which club?

460. Mick left Carrow Road in 1985 and joined which team?

ADAM DRURY

461. In what year was Adam born - 1976, 1978 or 1980?

462. Adam made his league debut at home to Grimsby in
      March 2001, but what was the score?

463. What award did Adam win during 2002/2003 whilst at
      Carrow Road?

464. Adam signed for Norwich in 2001, from which club?

465. Adam scored his first goal in August 2002 in a 1-1 away
      draw against which club?

466. In what position does Adam play for Norwich?

467. Which manager signed Adam and gave him his debut for
      Norwich?

468. In January 2005, Adam scored the equaliser in the 4-4
      home draw against which club?

469. Which squad number was Adam given during
      2006/2007?

470. When Norwich won the Championship in 2003/2004,
      what was extra-special for Adam?

WHERE DID THEY COME FROM? - 1

Match the player with his pre-Norwich club

471. Leon McKenzie   Bournemouth

472. Simon Charlton   Tottenham
                                     Hotspur

473. Phil Mulryne   Kilmarnock

474. Gary Holt   Oxford United

475. Mike Sheron   Peterborough
                                     United

476. Jimmy Neighbour   Manchester United

477. John Ryan   Manchester City

478. Tony Powell   Luton Town

479. Colin Suggett   Bolton Wanderers

480. Roger Gibbins   West Bromwich
                                     Albion

1993/1994

481. The first league win of the season was against Blackburn Rovers, winning 3-2, but which players scored the goals?

482. Which player scored four goals against Everton in a 5-1 away win during September?

483. Who wore squad number 10 during the season?

484. Who was the only player to play in all 42 league matches?

485. Which team did Norwich play on the final day of the season, drawing 1-1, causing the opponents to be relegated?

486. In what position in the league did Norwich finish?

487. Which club won the Premier League this season?

488. Who was the Canaries' top goalscorer with 25 league goals?

489. Against which club did Mark Robins score his only goal during the season?

490. Mike Walker started the season as Norwich manager, but who finished the season as manager?

GARY DOHERTY

491. In what year was Gary born - 1978, 1979 or 1980?

492. Which Norwich manager signed Gary for the Canaries?

493. Norwich signed Gary in 2004, from which club?

494. Which country has Gary represented at full international level?

495. What squad number did Gary wear during 2006/2007?

496. Gary made his Norwich league debut in August 2004, against which club?

497. Which team did Gary play for between 1997 and 2000?

498. Against which club did Gary score his first Norwich goal, in only his second league appearance?

499. What award did Gary win whilst at Norwich during 2005/2006?

500. Gary scored in a 3-2 home win against West Bromwich Albion in February 2005. Which two other players scored?

MALKY MACKAY

501. In what year was Malky born in Scotland - 1970, 1971 or 1972?

502. Malky made his Norwich debut in September 1998 in a 2-1 away defeat to which club?

503. From which Scottish team did Norwich sign Malky in 1998?

504. In what position did Malky play for Norwich?

505. Malky scored one goal for Norwich in his first season in a 2-1 home win, against which team?

506. Which manager signed Malky for Norwich?

507. In March 2004, Malky scored twice against Ipswich in a 3-1 home win, but which player scored the other goal for Norwich?

508. Against which team did Malky score in a 1-0 home win in April 2001?

509. In April 2004, Malky made his full international debut for Scotland, against which country?

510. Malky left Carrow Road and joined which London club in 2004?

ROBERT GREEN

511. In what year was Robert born - 1978, 1979 or 1980?

512. Which goalkeeper left in July 2001 to make Robert the Canaries' first choice?

513. Robert made his Norwich debut in 1999, against which team?

514. In what position does Robert play?

515. Robert made his full England debut in May 2005 against Colombia, but who did he replace at half-time?

516. When Robert made his Norwich debut, what was the score in the game?

517. Which England manager gave Robert his full international debut?

518. Which Norwich manager was in charge in 1999 and handed Robert his debut?

519. What squad number was Robert allocated for Norwich City for the 2006/2007 season, even though he did not even play a match for the Canaries - 1, 13 or 27?

520. Which Liverpool goalkeeper replaced Robert in the England World Cup squad in 2006 as Robert got injured in an England B international in May 2006?

TOP LEAGUE GOALSCORERS IN A SEASON

Match the player with the season in which he was top scorer

521.	1971/1972	Robert Fleck
522.	1976/1977	Kevin Drinkell
523.	1981/1982	Iwan Roberts
524.	1983/1984	Darren Eadie
525.	1986/1987	Chris Sutton
526.	1991/1992	Ken Foggo
527.	1993/1994	Iwan Roberts
528.	1996/1997	Viv Busby
529.	1998/1999	John Deehan
530.	2000/2001	Keith Bertschin

NORWICH V. WEST HAM UNITED

531. Which four players scored the goals in the 4-1 win on New Year's Day 1988?

532. In August 1994, Norwich beat West Ham 1-0 at Carrow Road, but who scored the goal?

533. Kevin Drinkell scored in a 2-0 away win in March 1987, but which Norwich captain got the other?

534. In December 1991, Norwich beat West Ham in the League Cup 2-1, but which player scored both goals?

535. In which year did Mark Farrington score against the Hammers in a 1-0 home win?

536. Which two players scored in a 2-1 home win in December 1988?

537. Norwich beat West Ham 2-1 in the League Cup (4th round) in December 1991, but which team did the Canaries play in the 5th round?

538. Which Welsh Norwich legend played for West Ham during 1996/1997?

539. During 1975/1976, which player scored both goals in the 1-0 home and away wins against West Ham?

540. Which ex-Hammer scored against West Ham in a 1-0 home win for Norwich in November 1976?

CRAIG BELLAMY

541. In what year was Craig born in Cardiff - 1977, 1979 or 1981?

542. Craig made his league debut in March 1997 in a 2-0 away defeat, against which club?

543. Craig made 84 league appearances, scoring how many goals?

544. Which manager gave Craig his Norwich debut?

545. Which country has Craig represented at full international level?

546. In August 2000, Craig left Carrow Road and signed for which club?

547. Against which country did Craig made his full international debut?

548. During 1997/1998, Craig made 30 league starts and 6 sub appearances, scoring how many goals for Norwich?

549. In August 1998, against which London club did Craig score a hat-trick in a 4-2 home win?

550. Which club did Craig sign for in 2006 from Blackburn Rovers?

NORWICH IN THE FA CUP

551. Which team did Norwich beat 3-0 at Carrow Road in February 1992, with David Phillips and Chris Sutton (2) scoring?

552. Who beat Norwich in the FA Cup semi-final in 1959, played at St Andrews, Birmingham?

553. Which player scored four goals in a 5-0 win against Newcastle United in March 1963?

554. Can you recall the four goalscorers that scored in the 4-1 4th round win in January 1961?

555. Which team did Norwich beat 8-0 in January 1989 in the 4th round?

556. Which striker scored in a 1-0 3rd round win in January 1993?

557. During the 1985 FA Cup, which side did Norwich play four times in the 3rd round, eventually beating them 1-0?

558. Which team did Norwich beat 2-1 in the quarter-final replay after extra-time in March 1992?

559. Following on from the previous question, which two players scored the goals?

560. In January 1962, Norwich beat Ipswich 2-1 in the 4th round replay, but who scored both goals?

NATIONALITIES

Match the player with his nationality

561.	Joe Royle	Irish
562.	David Williams	English
563.	Martin Peters	Scottish
564.	John Devine	English
565.	Youssef Safri	French
566.	Andy Townsend	Welsh
567.	Bryan Gunn	Irish
568.	Efan Ekoku	Moroccan
569.	David Phillips	Nigerian
570.	Mattieu Louis-Jean	Welsh

DAVE WATSON

571. Where in England was Dave born in 1961?

572. Dave made his Norwich debut as a 19-year-old in a 2-0 defeat to which club?

573. From which club did Norwich sign Dave for £100,000 in November 1980?

574. What was extra-special about Dave winning the League Cup with Norwich in 1985?

575. During the League Cup run, against which team did Dave score in the 2nd round?

576. In which season did Dave win Norwich 'Player of the Season'?

577. Dave made 212 league appearances for Norwich, scoring how many goals - 7, 11 or 15?

578. When Dave left Carrrow Road in August 1986, which club did he sign for?

579. Dave won 12 England caps in his career, but how many were won whilst at Carrow Road?

580. In what position did Dave play during his career?

ROBERT EARNSHAW

581. In what year was Robert born in Zambia - 1979, 1980 or 1981?

582. From which West Midlands team did Norwich sign Robert?

583. Which Norwich City manager signed Robert in 2006?

584. Robert made his Norwich debut against which team in a 2-1 home defeat?

585. Which country has Robert represented at full international level?

586. Robert made his international debut in May 2002, against which country?

587. Which team did Robert play for between 1997 and 2004?

588. Against which team did Robert score his first goals for Norwich in a 3-0 home win in February 2006?

589. Against which former side did Robert score in April 2006 in a 1-0 away win?

590. Norwich beat Queens Park Rangers at Carrow Road in April 2006, with Robert scoring two goals, but what was the final score?

1990s

591. In February 1992, Norwich beat Crystal Palace 4-3 away, but which players scored the goals?

592. Mark Robins scored Norwich's first ever Premier League hat-trick in a 3-2 away win, against which club?

593. Which two defenders captained Norwich during 1991/1992?

594. Against which London club did Norwich play on the opening day of the 1994/1995 Premier League season?

595. Norwich were unbeaten in their first three Premier League matches, but which three teams did they play?

596. Which centre forward finished as the Canaries' top goalscorer, with 13 league goals by 1997/1998?

597. In what position in Division 1 did Norwich finish in 1998/1999 - 2nd , 9th or 17th?

598. Which goalkeeper played the last four league games in the 1990/1991 season?

599. Which two players scored 30 league goals between them during 1996/1997?

600. Which player scored 17 league goals for Norwich during 1998/1999?

CRAIG FLEMING

601. In what year was Craig born - 1971, 1972 or 1973?

602. Craig scored in a 3-2 home win in February 2005, together with Gary Doherty and Damien Francis, but who was it against?

603. Against which team did Craig make his Norwich league debut in August 1997?

604. From which club did Norwich sign Craig in 1997?

605. Which Norwich manager signed Craig?

606. Craig scored his first Norwich goal in April 1998 in a 5-0 home win, against which team?

607. During the 2006/2007 season, which squad number did Craig wear?

608. Which team did Craig play for between 1990 and 1991?

609. In November 2005, Craig scored his only goal of the season for Norwich in a 2-2 draw. Which other player scored?

610. Against which team did Norwich play in Craig's testimonial in July 2006.

EFAN EKOKU

611. Where was Efan born in 1967 - Liverpool, Nottingham or Manchester?

612. In what year did Efan sign for Norwich?

613. Which manager signed Efan for Norwich, paying Bournemouth £500,000?

614. What nationality is Efan?

615. In February 1994, Efan scored against Arsenal in a 1-1 home draw, but which player scored for the opponents?

616. In what position did Efan play for Norwich?

617. Against which London team did Efan score in a 1-1 draw, with Mark Stein scoring for the visitors?

618. Efan made 37 league appearances for Norwich, scoring how many goals?

619. When Efan left Carrow Road in October 1994, which team did he sign for?

620. Which club did Efan go on loan to between 2000 and 2001 before joining them on a free transfer in 2001 and staying there until 2003?

POT LUCK - 2

621. Which former Manchester United, Coventry City and Aston Villa striker did Nigel Worthington sign for Norwich City in September 2006?

622. When Norwich played in Division 3 South during 1955/1956, which player scored 31 goals in 45 games?

623. As of 2006/2007, what colour was Norwich's away kit?

624. Can you name the two previous grounds used before moving to Carrow Road in 1935?

625. What is the fans' song called?

626. Against which team did Norwich record their first league win in the 2006/2007 season?

627. In what two years were Norwich League Cup runners-up?

628. Which club did Robert Green sign for when he left Carrow Road in August 2006?

629. Who managed Norwich during 1961/1962?

630. In which two seasons did Norwich win the Division 2 title?

IAN CULVERHOUSE

631.   In what year was Ian born - 1962, 1963 or 1964?

632.   Ian made his Norwich debut in October 1985 in the League Cup 2nd round in a 2-1 home win, against which club?

633.   Ian scored one goal for Norwich during 1993/1994 in a 3-0 home win, against which club?

634.   From which club did Norwich sign Ian in 1985?

635.   Ian made 296 league appearances, scoring how many goals?

636.   In what season did Ian win 'Player of the Season' for Norwich?

637.   What medal did Ian win in his first season at Norwich?

638.   Ian scored against Swindon Town in November 1988 in a 2-1 win in what competition?

639.   Which team did Ian join when he left Norwich in 1994, playing for them until 1998?

640.   During the 1993/1994 Premier League season, Ian was the only Norwich player to do what?

LEAGUE GOALSCORERS - 1

Match the player with the number of league goals scored

641.	Ken Burditt	57
642.	Ade Akinbiyi	10
643.	Neil Adams	2
644.	Les Eyre	31
645.	Jimmy Hill	62
646.	Noel Kinsey	25
647.	Duncan Forbes	58
648.	John Deelan	3
649.	Dale Gordon	55
650.	Gary Brooke	58

IWAN ROBERTS

651.   In what year was Iwan born - 1966, 1967 or 1968?

652.   What nationality is Iwan?

653.   From which club did Norwich sign Iwan in 1997 for £900,000?

654.   Against which club did Iwan score his first goal for Norwich in the League Cup?

655.   Iwan made his Norwich debut in August 1997 in a 2-0 home defeat, against which team?

656.   How many league goals did Iwan score in his first season at Carrow Road?

657.   Against which club did Iwan score a hat-trick in a 4-0 home win in February 2001?

658.   Iwan won Norwich 'Player of the Season' in 1998/1999, but in which season did he next win it?

659.   Against which club did Iwan score a brace in a 2-0 away win in March 2000?

660.   How many league goals did Iwan score during 2000/2001?

NORWICH V. LIVERPOOL

661. Which player scored the only goal in the 1-0 home win in May 1993?

662. Robert Fleck scored twice in the 3-0 home win in February 1992, but which player scored the other?

663. In December 1977 Norwich beat Liverpool 2-1 which players scored the goals?

664. Which player scored a league hat-trick for Norwich against Liverpool at Anfield in January 1962 in a 5-4 defeat?

665. In April 1994, Norwich beat Liverpool 1-0 at Anfield in the last ever match in front of the old Kop. Who scored the goal?

666. In 1989/1990, Liverpool were crowned champions for Division 1, but what was the score between the sides both home and away?

667. Which Danish midfield played for Liverpool during the 1980s and 1990s made his Norwich debut in December 1995?

668. In what year did Norwich beat Liverpool at Carrow Road in Liverpool's championship year, with captain Martin Peters scoring?

669. Which player scored twice against Liverpool in a 3-1 FA Cup win in January 1951, with Les Eyre scoring the other goal?

670. In April 1983, Norwich beat Liverpool at Anfield, but what was the score?

DARREN EADIE

671.   In what year was Darren born - 1971, 1973 or 1975?

672.   Darren scored a brace in a 2-0 win in May 1997, and was later sent off in the game, against which side?

673.   In October 1996, Norwich beat Grimsby 4-1 away, with Darren scoring two goals, but which players scored the other two?

674.   In what season did Darren win Norwich 'Player of the Season'?

675.   Darren finished as the club's highest league scorer during 1996/1997, with how many goals?

676.   Which Norwich manager gave Darren his Canaries' debut?

677.   Darren scored three league goals during 1998/1999, against which sides?

678.   Darren made 168 league appearances for Norwich, scoring how many goals?

679.   When Darren left Carrow Road in December 1999, which team did he join?

680.   How much did Norwich receive as a transfer fee from his new club?

NEIL ADAMS

681. Where was Neil born in 1965 - Sunderland, Stoke or Southend?

682. In what year did Neil sign for Norwich?

683. Neil scored on the opening day of the 1995/1996 season in a 3-1 away win against which team, with Jon Newsome scoring the other goals?

684. Neil made 182 league appearances, scoring how many goals?

685. In February 1997, Norwich drew 4-4 away to Charlton. Neil scored two of the goals, but which player scored the other two?

686. Which top-flight team did Neil play for between 1986 and 1989?

687. Neil played in 45 division games during 1996/1997, scoring how many goals -11, 13 or 15?

688. From which team did Norwich sign Neil, where he subsequently returned when he left Carrow Road?

689. Neil scored the only winning goal twice in August 1996. Can you name the two sides he scored against?

690. Against which team did Neil make his Canaries debut in a 3-3 away draw in the Premier League?

KEVIN KEELAN

691. In which country was Kevin born in 1941?

692. How many appearances did Kevin make for Norwich, a club record?

693. In what position did Kevin play for the Canaries?

694. Which Welsh-based side did Kevin sign for in 1963?

695. In 1974, Kevin had his Norwich testimonial, against which team?

696. Which team did Kevin play for in Trevor Brooking's testimonial in 1977?

697. What award did Kevin win at Norwich during 1972/1973 and 1973/1974?

698. Against which team did Kevin play his final Norwich match in 1980 in a 5-3 defeat?

699. Against which team did Kevin make his Norwich debut?

700. Which American side did Kevin sign for in 1981?

BIG WINS

Match the game with Norwich's winning score

701. **Torquay United**
     League Cup 2nd Round (Sept 1995)   *8-0*

702. **Huddersfield Town**
     Division 1 (Mar 1998)   *6-1*

703. **Watford**
     Division 1 (Apr 1984)   *5-1*

704. **Stockport County**
     Division 1 (Feb 2001)   *5-3*

705. **Millwall**
     Division 2 (Dec 1985)   *4-2*

706. **Birmingham City**
     Division 1 (Sept 1982)   *5-0*

707. **Sutton United**
     FA Cup 4th round (Jan 1989)   *6-1*

708. **Aston Villa**
     Division 1 (Aug 1975)   *5-1*

709. **Everton**
     Premier League (Sept 1993)   *4-0*

710. **Arsenal**
     Premier League (Aug 1982)   *6-1*

ALAN BLACK

711. In what year was Alan born in Dumbarton - 1941, 1943 or 1945?

712. Which manager brought Alan to Carrow Road, making him the manager's first signing?

713. Alan made his debut in a 2-1 away win against Northampton Town, but which players scored the goals?

714. Against which team did Alan score his first league goal in a 4-1 away defeat in November 1972?

715. How many league goals did Alan score in his 176 appearances?

716. From which team did Alan sign to join Norwich in 1966?

717. In what position did Norwich finish in Division 2 in Alan's first season at Carrow Road - 7th, 9th or 11th?

718. In what position did Alan play for the Canaries?

719. What is Alan's middle name - David, Douglas or Derek?

720. In which year did Alan play his final Norwich City game?

LEAGUE APPEARANCES - 2

*Match up the player with the number of
league appearances he made*

721.	Kevin Keelan	84 (6)
722.	Bryan Gunn	592
723.	Darren Eadie	571
724.	Ron Ashman	417 (2)
725.	Justin Fashanu	101
726.	Dave Stringer	390
727.	Sandy Keennon	11
728.	Joe Hannah	153 (15)
729.	Willie Donachie	398
730.	Norman Wharton	213

MICK PHELAN

731. In what year was Mick born - 1962, 1964 or 1966?

732. Against which team did Mick make his Norwich debut in August 1985 in a 1-0 win at Carrow Road?

733. What was extra-special when Mick scored his three league goals for Norwich during 1985/1986?

734. In July 1985, Mick signed from which club to join Norwich?

735. Which manager signed Mike for Norwich?

736. Norwich beat Aston Villa 4-1 in September 1986 at Villa Park, with Mick on the score sheet, but which three players scored the other goals?

737. Mick made 156 league appearances, scoring how many goals for Norwich?

738. Against which London club did Mike score in a 1-0 home win in September 1988?

739. To whom was Mick appointed assistant Norwich manager in December 1995?

740. In the summer of 1989, Mick left Carrow Road and signed for which club?

RON SAUNDERS

741. In what year was Ron born in Birkenhead - 1922, 1932 or 1942?

742. During Ron's playing career, in which position did he play?

743. What team did Ron manage before Norwich City?

744. In what year did Ron take over as Norwich's manager?

745. Can you name the three Midlands clubs that Ron managed in his managerial career?

746. Which special achievement did Ron realise in 1973 with Norwich City?

747. Which team was Ron playing for when he won the Third Division Championship in 1962?

748. Ron led Norwich to promotion to Division 1 in 1972, but how many of the 42 league games did they win - 13, 17 or 21?

749. Which manager took over at Carrow Road when Ron left?

750. In which year did Ron leave Carrow Road to join Manchester City a few days later?

WHERE DID THEY COME FROM? - 2

Match the player with his pre-Norwich club

751.	Darren Huckerby	Colchester United
752.	Terry Anderson	Leyton Orient
753.	Colin Sullivan	Manchester City
754.	Mathias Svensson	Sheffield United
755.	Jurgen Colin	Arsenal
756.	Duncan Forbes	Oldham Athletic
757.	Keith Robson	Plymouth Argyle
758.	Carl Bradshaw	PSV Eindhoven
759.	Phil Hoadley	Cardiff City
760.	Andy Linighan	Charlton Athletic

MANAGERS

Match the manager with his period in charge of Norwich

761.	Mike Walker	1995-1996
762.	Bruce Rioch	1980-1987
763.	Martin O'Neill	1996-1998
764.	Ron Ashman	1994-1995
765.	Mike Walker	1998-2000
766.	Dave Stringer	1962-1966
767.	John Deehan	1995
768.	Gary Megson	1969-1973
769.	Ken Brown	1992-1994
770.	Ron Saunders	1987-1992

NIGEL WORTHINGTON

771. In what year was Nigel born - 1959, 1960 or 1961?

772. In what position did Nigel play during his playing career?

773. Nigel led Norwich to promotion during 2003/2004 with a record number of points - how many?

774. What nationality is Nigel?

775. When the board appointed Nigel as Norwich manager, which two coaches did he work with?

776. Which team did Nigel play for between 1984 and 1994?

777. How many international games did Nigel play for his country?

778. In what year did Nigel leave Carrow Road as manager?

779. During 2003/2004, which two strikers did Nigel sign on loan, one from Manchester City and the other from Aston Villa?

780. In January 2005, which player did Nigel sign for a club record fee?

GARY HOLT

781. In what year was Gary born - 1971, 1972 or 1973?

782. From which Scottish club did Norwich sign Gary in 2001?

783. Against which team did Gary make his debut in March 2001?

784. What nationality is Gary?

785. In which position did Gary play?

786. In what season did Gary win Norwich 'Player of the Season'?

787. When Gary left Carrow Road, which team did he sign for in 2006?

788. In Gary's first season at Carrow Road (2000/2001), what squad number did he wear?

789. In February 2004, Norwich beat Coventry 2-0 away with Gary scoring, but who scored the other goal?

790. In December 2001, Norwich beat Sheffield Wednesday away with Gary scoring, but what was the score in the game?

NORWICH IN THE LEAGUE CUP

791.   Ashley Ward scored a hat-trick against Bradford (away) in November 1995, but what was the score (after extra time)?

792.   Which London team did Norwich beat 3-0 on aggregate in the semi-final to reach the final in 1973?

793.   Which side did Norwich beat 4-1 on aggregate in the 1962 final?

794.   In October 1962, Norwich beat Carlisle United 5-0 in a 3rd round replay, but who scored a hat-trick in the game?

795.   Against which club did Norwich play in the final in March 1973, losing 1-0 at Wembley?

796.   Norwich beat Blackpool 5-0 in a 2nd round tie in October 2000, but which players scored the goals?

797.   Which player captained Norwich to the 1975 final against Aston Villa?

798.   Which London club knocked Norwich out of the competition during 1991/1992?

799.   Which player scored a hat-trick against Cardiff City in October 1983 in the 2nd round in a 3-0 home win?

800.   Which club did Norwich beat 7-1 in the 4th round in November 1963?

POT LUCK - 3

801. Who is the oldest player to have played a competitive match for Norwich at the age of 42?

802. Who is Norwich's record goalscorer with 122 league goals in his career between 1945 and 1958?

803. In which season did Norwich win Division 3 (South)?

804. Which player signed for Norwich during July 2006 from Manchester City for £600,000?

805. Simon Charlton left Carrrow Road in August 2006, but which team did he join?

806. Who managed Norwich between 1957 and 1961?

807. Which three players scored the goals in the 3-2 home win in August 2006 against Luton Town?

808. Which player won Norwich 'Player of the Season' during 1980/1981?

809. When Andy Linighan left Norwich, which team did he join?

810. Which player did Norwich sign in June 1994 from Leeds United?

BRUCE RIOCH

811.   In what year was Bruce born - 1943, 1945 or 1947?

812.   What nationality is Bruce, who also represented his country at international level?

813.   In what year was Bruce appointed Norwich manager?

814.   For which club did Bruce make his league debut in 1964?

815.   Which London club did Bruce manage between 1995 and 1996?

816.   When Bruce was appointed as manager of Norwich, who was appointed Norwich's Director of Football?

817.   At which Danish club did Bruce take over as manager in 2005?

818.   How many caps did Bruce win for his country - 20, 22 or 24?

819.   At which club was Bruce's first managerial appointment?

820.   In what year did Bruce leave Carrow Road as manager?

MIKE WALKER

821. During Mike's playing career, in which position did he play?

822. In his first season in charge of Norwich Mike led them to their highest ever position, but what was it?

823. Mike managed Norwich for the first time in the league against which team?

824. In what year was Mike appointed manager (first spell)?

825. What nationality is Mike - Welsh, Irish or Italian?

826. When Mike left Carrow Road in 1994, he became manager of which Premier League team?

827. In what year did Mike sign professional forms with Reading, subsequently failing to make the first team?

828. In which year was Mike appointed manager of Colchester United, only to be sacked the year after - 1985, 1986 or 1987?

829. What is the name of Mike's son, the former England and Spurs goalkeeper?

830. Mike managed Norwich again in 1996, but what year did he leave Carrow Road?

LEAGUE GOALSCORERS - 2

Match the player with the number of league goals scored

831.	John Deehan	51
832.	Johnny Gavin	106
833.	Ted MacDougall	56
834.	Chris Sutton	1
835.	Terry Allcock	32
836.	Tony Cottee	44
837.	Ralph Hunt	62
838.	Martin Peters	122
839.	Robert Fleck	35
840.	Craig Bellamy	67

CAPS FOR MY COUNTRY

Match the player with the number of caps won

841. Chris Woods   6 Scottish caps

842. Nigel Worthington   35 Welsh caps

843. Martin Peters   1 England cap

844. Joe Royle   4 Scottish caps

845. Bryan Gunn   43 England caps

846. Chris Sutton   67 England caps

847. Mark Bowen   64 Northern
Ireland caps

848. Robert Fleck   15 Welsh caps

849. Iwan Roberts   66 Northern
Ireland caps

850. Martin O'Neill   6 England caps

PAUL HAYLOCK

851. Paul was born in Lowestoft, in what year?

852. Against which Midlands team did Paul score in the FA Cup 3rd round replay in January 1985?

853. In how many league games did Paul score in his 155 appearances?

854. Against which team did Paul score his only league goal of the 1982/1983 season?

855. In what year did Paul make his Norwich debut?

856. In what position did Paul play for Norwich?

857. Which medal did Paul win with Norwich in 1985?

858. Paul left Carrow Road in August 1986 and signed for which team?

859. What nationality is Paul - Irish, Welsh or English?

860. Paul scored in a 2-2 home draw to Aston Villa in March 1985, but which other Norwich player scored?

NORWICH V. MANCHESTER UNITED

861. Which Norwich players scored in the 2-2 away draw in December 1993?

862. Norwich first beat Manchester United in the league at Old Trafford in what year?

863. Which player scored a brace in a 2-0 home win in January 1990?

864. In April 2005, Norwich beat United at Carrow Road, but what was the score?

865. Who captained Norwich during 1988/1989 and scored in the 2-1 away win during October 1988?

866. When Manchester United won the first Premier League title in 1992/1993, how many points did Norwich win in both games, home and away?

867. In April 1977, Norwich beat United 2-1, but which two Canaries players scored?

868. What was the score between the sides when they met in the League Cup in September 1979?

869. During 1988/1989, who finished higher in Division 1, Norwich City or Manchester United?

870. In which year did Ted MacDougall score two goals in a 2-0 home win against United?

1994/1995

871. Norwich got their first three points at home, winning 1-0, against which side?

872. In October, which London team did Norwich beat 4-2 at Carrow Road?

873. Against which two sides did Robert Ullathorne score during the season?

874. What was the score when Norwich entertained rivals Ipswich Town at Carrow Road?

875. Who was the top league goalscorer with eight goals?

876. Can you name the three goalkeepers that played during the season (in all competitions)?

877. Norwich finished in 20th place and were relegated along with which three other teams?

878. In December, Norwich beat Chelsea 3-0 at Carrow Road, but which players scored?

879. Which player captained the team for most of the season?

880. Which team won the Premier League, with ex-Norwich player Tim Sherwood picking up a winners medal?

NORWICH V. SPURS

881.   What was the score when the sides met for the first time
       in the Premier League in December 1992 at Carrow
       Road?

882.   Which two players scored for Norwich after coming back
       from 2-0 down to draw 2-2 in Division 1 in September
       1989?

883.   What was the score in the league at Carrow Road in
       December 1983?

884.   Which two strikers scored the goals when Norwich beat
       Spurs 3-1 at White Hart Lane in December 1993?

885.   Norwich beat Spurs 4-0 in August 1979, with Kevin
       Reeves scoring two, and which other two players scoring
       a goal apiece?

886.   In October 1972, the sides met at Carrow Road and drew
       2-2, but who scored both goals for Norwich?

887.   Can you name the three players that scored in the 3-1
       home league win in October 1988?

888.   Which player captained the team and scored in the 3-2
       away win in April 1981?

889.   Norwich finished 12th in the league during 1993/1994,
       but did Spurs finish higher or lower than Norwich?

890.   Which Spurs player scored when Tottenham beat
       Norwich in the 1973 Cup final?

KEN BROWN

891. In what Cup did Ken guide Norwich to victory against Sunderland in 1985 in a 1-0 win?

892. Which Norwich manager did Ken take over from?

893. For what London team did Ken make his debut in 1952?

894. Walter Winterbottom gave Ken his only England cap against which national side?

895. In what year was Ken appointed Norwich manager?

896. Where was Ken born in 1934 - London, Manchester or Liverpool?

897. Which team did Ken manage between 1988 and 1990?

898. In 1964, which Cup did Ken win as a member of the West Ham team?

899. Ken was appointed assistant manager to whom in 1970 at Bournemouth?

900. When Ken left Carrow Road as manager, who took over?

KEVIN BOND

901. In what year was Kevin born in London - 1955, 1956 or 1957?

902. Kevin made his Norwich league debut as a substitute in a 0-0 draw in April 1976, against which side?

903. In what position did Kevin play in his career?

904. During 1979/1980, which award did Kevin win whilst at Carrow Road?

905. Can you name the two sides that Kevin scored against in the league during 1978/1979?

906. How many league goals did Kevin score in his 142 league appearances?

907. Against which team did Kevin score a brace in a 2-1 home win in August 1979?

908. In May 1998, Kevin was named assistant manager to whom at Portsmouth?

909. What is Kevin's middle name - Joshua, James or John?

910. Kevin scored against which side in a 2-2 home draw in December 1980, with John Fashanu getting the other goal?

1960s

911. Which player scored 26 league goals in 38 games during 1963/1964?

912. Norwich beat Cardiff 4-2 away in August 1962, but which two players scored a brace in the game?

913. Norwich played in Division 2 during 1960/1961 and finished in 4th place, but which team won the league?

914. Against which club did Hugh Curran score a league hat-trick in a 4-2 home win in October 1967?

915. Can you name the two Norwich goalkeepers that played during 1968/1969?

916. Who scored 16 league goals in 26 appearances during 1960/1961?

917. Did Norwich finish higher or lower than Ipswich Town in Division 2 during 1965/1966?

918. Which player finished as City's top league goalscorer in 1966/1967 with 16 goals?

919. During 1964/1965, which player scored three league goals in only four appearances?

920. Who wore the number 3 shirt and captained the team in every game during 1960/1961?

DARREN HUCKERBY

921. Darren was born in Nottingham in what year?

922. Which manager signed Darren for Norwich in 2003?

923. At which club did Darren start his league career during 1993/1994?

924. What nationality is Darren - Welsh, Irish or English?

925. Norwich beat Barnsley 5-1 at Carrow Road in August 2006, Darren scored one goal, can you name the three other goalscorers (one player scored two goals)?

926. Which squad number did Darren wear during 2006/2007?

927. In what season did Darren win Norwich 'Player of the Season'?

928. For which team did Darren play between 2000 and 2003?

929. On 12 August 2006, Norwich beat which team 3-2 in the Championship with Darren scoring?

930. Darren made his Norwich debut (whilst on loan) at home to Burnley in September 2003, which two City players scored the goals in the 2-0 league win?

PAUL McVEIGH

931.   Where was Paul born in 1977 - Dublin, Belfast or London?

932.   Against what team did Paul score his only goal of the 2000/2001 in February 2001?

933.   In which year did Paul sign from Tottenham Hotspur to join Norwich?

934.   What nationality is Paul?

935.   During Norwich's Premier League season 2004/2005, Paul scored one league goal, against which team?

936.   Which team did Paul score a penalty against in the 3rd round of the FA Cup in January 2006 in a 2-1 home defeat?

937.   In December 2005, which team did Norwich beat 2-1 away, with Paul scoring both goals?

938.   What is Paul's middle name - Frank, Francis or Freddie?

939.   In what position does Paul play?

940.   During 2006/2007, which squad number did Paul wear?

NORWICH V. SOUTHAMPTON

941. When the sides met for the first time in the Premier League, Norwich won 1-0 at Carrow Road, but who scored?

942. Which two players scored in a 2-1 League Cup 4th round win in November 1973?

943. In August 1978, Norwich played Southampton at Carrow Road on the opening day of the season, but what was the score?

944. On New Year's Day 1994, the two sides met at the Dell, but what was the score?

945. Which four players scored when Norwich beat Southampton 4-3 in August 1986?

946. Which two players scored two goals apiece in a 5-2 away win in April 1956?

947. In January 1985, Norwich beat Southampton 1-0, but who scored the goal?

948. Which players scored in the 2-1 FA Cup quarter-final win in March 1992 at Carrow Road?

949. Which player, wearing the number 11 shirt, scored the only goal in a 1-0 home win during April 1963?

950. During 1987/1988, Norwich finished 14th in Division 1, but did Southampton finish higher or lower than the Canaries?

MATT JACKSON

951. In what year was Matt born in Yorkshire - 1967, 1969 or 1971?

952. From which club did manager Mike Walker sign Matt?

953. In what season did Matt win Norwich 'Player of the Season'?

954. Matt made his Norwich debut in December 1996, against which London club?

955. In Matt's first season at Carrow Road he scored two goals, against which clubs?

956. During 1999/2000, which player captained the team in Matt's absence on eight league occasions?

957. Against which team did Matt score in April 1998, together with Iwan Roberts, Craig Bellamy, Chris Llewellyn and Neil Fenn, in a 5-0 home win?

958. Matt scored one league goal during 1998/1999 in a 4-2 home win in August, against which London team?

959. When did Matt captain Norwich for the first time - in his first or second season at Carrow Road?

960. When Matt left Carrow Road, which team did he join?

DARYL SUTCH

961. In what year was Daryl born - 1969, 1970 or 1971?

962. In August 1997, Daryl scored in a 1-0 away win against which north-east side?

963. Daryl made his Norwich league debut in a 3-0 defeat in December 1990, against which club?

964. Can you name the three league teams that Daryl scored against during 1996/1997?

965. Daryl scored two league goals in Norwich's first Premier League season, against which two sides?

966. Which squad number did Daryl wear during the 1994/1995 Premier League season?

967. How many league goals did Daryl score during his Norwich career?

968. Daryl scored in a 2-1 home win against Leicester City in November 1994, but which other Canary scored in the match?

969. Which two sides did Norwich beat 1-0, with Daryl scoring the winning goals in both games?

970. Which team did Daryl sign for when he left Carrow Road?

JUSTIN FASHANU

971.   In what year was Justin born in London - 1959, 1960 and 1961?

972.   In what position did Justin play for the Canaries?

973.   Justin started 13 league games and made 3 sub appearances during 1978/1979, scoring how many goals - 1, 5 or 9?

974.   Justin won 'BBC Goal of the Season' in 1980, but against which team did he score the goal?

975.   Justin scored a league hat-trick in Division 1 in August 1980, against which team?

976.   Against which team did Justin score a brace on the opening day of the 1979/1980 season, with Norwich winning 4-2?

977.   When Justin left Carrow Road, which club did he join, costing £1 million?

978.   How many league goals did Justin score in his 40 league starts during 1980/1981?

979.   How many goals did Justin score for Norwich in his 90 league appearances?

980.   Justin scored one league goal during 1981/1982 against Derby County in November 1981, but which other players scored?

1980s

981. Which London club did Norwich beat 6-1 at Carrow Road during December 1985?

982. During 1988/1989, Norwich finished 4th in Division 1, but which team won the title?

983. How many League games did Norwich win during 1983/1984 in Division One - 6, 12 or 18?

984. During 1982/1983, which three players shared the Canaries captaincy?

985. Norwich won the title of Division 2 during 1985/1986, but how many of the 42 league games did they win - 20, 25 or 30?

986. Apart from the League Cup and FA Cup, in which other Cup competition did Norwich compete in during 1985/1986?

987. In what position did Norwich finish in Division 2 during 1981/1982?

988. Which team did Norwich beat 6-1 at home in April 1984, with John Deehan scoring four goals?

989. Who were the only two players to play in every league game during 1982/1983?

990. During 1981/1982, Keith Bertschin finished as top league goalscorer with 12 goals, but which two players finished with 10 goals each?

NORWICH V. CHELSEA

991. In December 1994, Norwich beat Chelsea 3-0, but which two players scored the goals?

992. What was the score when the sides met at Carrow Road in December 1987?

993. Norwich beat Chelsea 2-1 at Stamford Bridge on the final day of the season in May 1985, but which players scored for the Canaries?

994. Norwich beat Chelsea 2-1 in their first meeting in the premier league in August 1992, but who scored the goals?

995. During the 1993/1994 season, Norwich finished 12th, but did Chelsea finish higher or lower than the Canaries?

996. When the sides met in April 1973 at Carrow Road, who scored the only goal in the 1-0 win?

997. In December 1972, a League Cup tie was abandoned after Norwich were leading 3-2. What was the reason for the game being abandoned?

998. Norwich beat Chelsea 4-1 in Division 2 at Carrow Road in April 1963, but which player scored a brace?

999. Which striker played for Norwich in the early 1990s and signed for Chelsea in 1999?

1000. Norwich beat Chelsea 2-0 away in the 1st leg of the 1973 semi-final League Cup tie, but what was the score in the 2nd leg?

ANSWERS

HISTORY OF THE CLUB

1.   1905
2.   The Canaries
3.   Leicester City
4.   Mark Bowen
5.   Crewe Alexandra
6.   33
7.   Ron Ashman
8.   1993
9.   John Bowman
10.   Coventry City

BRYAN GUNN

11.   1963
12.   477
13.   6
14.   Egypt
15.   Aberdeen
16.   Tottenham Hotspur
17.   Ken Brown
18.   2
19.   Hibernian
20.   Andy Roxburgh

1986/1987

21.   Kevin Drinkell
22.   Graham Benstead and Bryan Gunn
23.   Millwall
24.   5th
25.   Southampton, Aston Villa and West Ham United
26.   Aston Villa
27.   Steve Bruce
28.   17
29.   Chelsea
30.   Ian Crook and Trevor Putney

NATIONALITIES

31.   Dickson Etuhu   Nigerian

32.	Robert Green	English
33.	Mark Bowen	Welsh
34.	Jurgen Colin	Dutch
35.	Alan Black	Scottish
36.	Mal Lucas	Welsh
37.	Chris Sutton	English
38.	Bobby Brennan	Irish
39.	Darren Huckerby	English
40.	Michael Spillane	Irish

MARK BOWEN

41. 1963
42. Tottenham Hotspur
43. Ken Brown
44. Left back (defender)
45. 25
46. 1989/1990
47. Wales
48. Steve Bruce
49. 2-1 to Norwich City
50. West Ham United

2005/2006

51. Plymouth Argyle
52. 1-1
53. Darren Huckerby and Robert Earnshaw (2)
54. 9th
55. Dean Ashton
56. Sheffield United
57. Milton Keynes Dons
58. Nigel Worthington
59. Robert Earnshaw and Leon McKenzie
60. Robert Earnshaw (v. Cardiff City)

JOHN DEEHAN

61. 1957
62. 15
63. Watford

64.   League Cup Winners Medal
65.   62
66.   Centre forward
67.   Aston Villa and West Bromwich Albion
68.   Luton Town
69.   Charlton Athletic
70.   Ipswich Town

UEFA CUP - 1993/1994

71.   Vitesse Arnhem
72.   John Polston, Jeremy Goss and Efan Ekoku
73.   Mark Bowen and Jeremy Goss
74.   Bryan Gunn, Ian Culverhouse, Mark Bowen, Ian Butterworth, Spencer Prior, Rob Newman, Mark Robins, Ian Crook, Chris Sutton, Ruel Fox and Jeremy Goss
75.   Bryan Gunn
76.   Jeremy Goss
77.   Jeremy Goss
78.   Mike Walker
79.   6
80.   Inter Milan

LEAGUE APPEARANCES - 1

81.	Terry Allcock	334 (5)
82.	Roy McCrohan	385
83.	Peter Grant	64 (4)
84.	Tony Cottee	5 (2)
85.	Ken Nethercott	378
86.	Bobby Brennan	225
87.	Steve Walford	93
88.	Mark Bowen	315 (5)
89.	Colin Suggett	200 (3)
90.	Ian Crook	314 (27)

WHERE DID THEY GO? - 1

91.	John Polston	Reading
92.	Matt Jackson	Wigan Athletic
93.	Chris Sutton	Blackburn Rovers

94.	Jim Brennan	Southampton
95.	Darel Russell	Stoke City
96.	Viv Busby	Stoke City
97.	Rob Newman	Southend United
98.	Keith O'Neill	Middlesbrough
99.	Paul Dalglish	Wigan Athletic
100.	Clint Easton	Wycombe Wanderers

CHRIS WOODS

101.	1959
102.	Queens Park Rangers
103.	£225,000
104.	Wolverhampton Wanderers
105.	England
106.	1983/1984
107.	216
108.	Ken Brown
109.	43
110.	Everton

NORWICH CITY V. IPSWICH TOWN

111.	Hugh Curran
112.	Malky Mackay
113.	John Ryan
114.	2-1
115.	John Polston and Andy Johnson (2)
116.	Darren Huckerby
117.	John Miller
118.	3-0 to Norwich City
119.	Jeremy Goss
120.	Leon McKenzie

IAN BUTTERWORTH

121.	1964
122.	4-1
123.	4
124.	Nottingham Forest

125.   8
126.   Centre back (defender)
127.   Badminton, cricket and table tennis
128.   Millwall
129.   Liverpool
130.   Darlington

POSITION IN THE LEAGUE - 1

131.	2005/2006	9th
132.	2003/2004	1st
133.	2001/2002	6th
134.	1999/2000	12th
135.	1997/1998	15th
136.	1995/1996	16th
137.	1993/1994	12th
138.	1991/1992	18th
139.	1989/1990	10th
140.	1987/1988	14th

NORWICH CITY V. ARSENAL

141.   4-2 to Norwich City
142.   Mark Bowen and Ruel Fox
143.   John Deehan
144.   Graham Paddon
145.   Ian Crook and Trevor Putney
146.   3-1
147.   2-1 to Norwich City
148.   David Rocastle
149.   1954 (January)
150.   John Deehan (2) and Keith Bertschin

NORWICH IN THE LEAGUE CUP

151.   Terry Allcock
152.   Chris Woods, Paul Haylock, Dennis Van Wijk, Steve Bruce, Peter Mendham, Dave Watson, Mark Barham, Mike Channon, John Deehan, Asa Hartford and Louie Donowa
153.   Arsenal and Chelsea
154.   Gordon Chisholm

155. Hugh Curran
156. Ashley Ward
157. Aston Villa
158. Wolverhampton Wanderers
159. 4-1 (3-1 and 1-0)
160. Kevin Keelan, Mel Machin, Colin Sullivan, Peter Morris, Duncan Forbes, Dave Stringer, John Miller, Ted MacDougall, Phil Boyer, Colin Suggett and Tony Powell

POT LUCK - 1
161. Efan Ekoku
162. 1995
163. The Canaries
164. 1962
165. Archie Macaulay
166. Yellow & Green
167. Ian Davies (v. Birmingham City)
168. Ken Foggo
169. Terry Allcock
170. 1993

MARTIN O'NEILL
171. 1952
172. Birmingham City
173. 1995
174. Midfielder/Forward
175. 64
176. Wycombe Wanderers
177. Leicester City
178. Northern Irish
179. OBE
180. Aston Villa

1970s
181. Martin Peters
182. League Cup and Texaco Cup
183. John Ryan and David Jones
184. Ted MacDougall (17) and Phil Boyer (16)

185. Leicester City
186. Peter Silvester and Ken Foggo
187. Dave Stringer
188. Mel Machin
189. Kevin Keelan
190. David Cross

WHERE DID THEY GO? - 2

191.	Daryl Sutch	Southend United
192.	Thomas Helveg	Borussia Monchengladbach
193.	Max Briggs	Oxford United
194.	Tony Spearing	Leicester City
195.	Robert Green	West Ham United
196.	Erik Fuglestad	Viking Stavanger
197.	Jamie Cureton	Bristol Rovers
198.	Ian Davies	Newcastle United
199.	Dean Ashton	West Ham United
200.	Roger Brown	Fulham

TIM SHERWOOD

201. 1969
202. 1989
203. Queens Park Rangers
204. Robert Fleck and Robert Rosario (2)
205. 3
206. Midfield (centre)
207. 7
208. 10
209. Sunderland
210. Blackburn Rovers

GARY MEGSON

211. 1959
212. Manchester City
213. 3rd
214. 1996
215. Mike Walker
216. Nottingham Forest

217.   Manchester City
218.   Plymouth Argyle
219.   Norwich City (1995/1996)
220.   West Bromwich Albion

2004/2005

221.   Crystal Palace
222.   Southampton
223.   Damien Francis
224.   Dean Ashton
225.   19th
226.   Damien Francis, Dean Ashton, Leon McKenzie and Adam Drury
227.   Nigel Worthington
228.   Patrick Kluivert
229.   Mathias Svensson
230.   Dean Ashton and Leon McKenzie

RUEL FOX

231.   Ipswich
232.   Ken Brown
233.   Mark Robins (2) and David Phillips
234.   14
235.   Leeds United
236.   West Bromwich Albion
237.   22
238.   Newcastle United
239.   West Ham United and Arsenal
240.   Derby County, Aston Villa and Arsenal

NORWICH & IPSWICH CONNECTIONS

241.   Andy Marshall
242.   Sammy Chung
243.   Louie Donowa
244.   Joe Royle
245.   John Deehan
246.   Clive Baker
247.   Steve Foley
248.   Keith Bertschin

249. Trevor Putney
250. Willie Donachie

JEREMY GOSS

251. 1965
252. Wimbledon and Aston Villa
253. Coventry City
254. Crystal Palace
255. Wales
256. Crystal Palace
257. 14
258. Chelsea and Tottenham Hotspur
259. Vitesse Arnhem and Bayern Munich
260. 6

WHO AM I?

261. Ruel Fox
262. Chris Woods
263. Craig Fleming
264. Martin Chivers
265. Tim Sherwood
266. Mark Robins
267. Chris Sutton
268. Jeremy Goss
269. Mick Channon
270. Neil Adams

JOHN POLSTON

271. 1968
272. Tottenham Hotspur
273. English
274. 3-2 to Norwich
275. 10
276. 200 (15) = 215
277. Crystal Palace
278. 4
279. Tranmere Rovers
280. Reading

CHRIS SUTTON

281. 1973
282. Queens Park Rangers
283. 1993/1994
284. Cameroon
285. Blackburn Rovers
286. The Premiership
287. 43
288. Leeds United
289. Celtic
290. 25

1992/1993 - THE FIRST PREMIER LEAGUE SEASON

291. Manchester United (1st) and Aston Villa (2nd)
292. Mike Walker
293. Arsenal
294. 2-0 to Ipswich Town
295. Mark Bowen, Bryan Gunn and David Phillips
296. Mark Robins
297. Leeds United
298. Efan Ekoku
299. Aston Villa
300. Mark Robins, Ian Crook and Lee Power

NORWICH LEAGUE CUP WINNERS - 1985

301. Sunderland
302. 1-0
303. Ipswich Town
304. John Deehan
305. Ken Brown
306. Asa Hartford
307. John Deehan
308. Preston North End
309. Wembley
310. Peter Mendham

ROB NEWMAN

311. 1963

312. Dave Stringer
313. Sheffield United
314. Defender (central)
315. Carl Bradshaw
316. Bristol City
317. Motherwell and Wigan Athletic
318. Southend United
319. Sheffield Wednesday and Blackburn Rovers
320. 14

IAN CROOK
321. Luton Town
322. Chelsea
323. Tottenham Hotspur
324. England
325. 18
326. Tottenham Hotspur
327. Midfield
328. Arsenal
329. Tottenham Hotspur
330. FA Cup (3rd round)

MIKE MILLIGAN
331. 1967
332. Ipswich Town
333. John Deehan
334. Midfield
335. Aston Villa and Everton
336. 5
337. Charlton Athletic
338. 20th
339. Millwall and Portsmouth
340. Blackpool

DIVISION 1 CHAMPIONS - 2003/2004
341. Mathias Svensson (2), Darren Huckerby (2) and Leon McKenzie
342. Cardiff City
343. Rotherham

344. 28
345. Nigel Worthington
346. Sunderland
347. 94
348. Craig Fleming, Malky Mackay, Paul McVeigh and Leon McKenzie
349. Preston North End
350. Crewe Alexandra

ROBERT FLECK

351. Glasgow
352. Glasgow Rangers
353. 10
354. Chelsea
355. 1991/1992
356. Wimbledon
357. 56
358. Port Vale and Oxford United
359. 10
360. Sutton United

PLAYER OF THE SEASON

361.	2005/2006	Gary Doherty
362.	2003/2004	Craig Fleming
363.	2000/2001	Andy Marshall
364.	1998/1999	Iwan Roberts
365.	1994/1995	Jon Newsome
366.	1990/1991	Ian Culverhouse
367.	1987/1988	Bryan Gunn
368.	1984/1985	Steve Bruce
369.	1976/1977	Martin Peters
370.	1973/1974	Kevin Keelan

STEVE BRUCE

371. 1960
372. Liverpool
373. 14
374. Gillingham
375. Norwich 'Player of the Season'

376. *1986/1987*
377. *8*
378. **Coventry City and Watford**
379. **Birmingham City**
380. **Manchester United**

POSITION IN THE LEAGUE - 2

381.	*1985/1986*	*1st*
382.	*1983/1984*	*14th*
383.	*1981/1982*	*3rd*
384.	*1979/1980*	*12th*
385.	*1977/1978*	*13th*
386.	*1975/1976*	*10th*
387.	*1973/1974*	*22nd*
388.	*1971/1972*	*1st*
389.	*1969/1970*	*11th*
390.	*1967/1968*	*9th*

DALE GORDON

391. *1967*
392. **Liverpool**
393. *1984*
394. *1988/1989*
395. **Stoke City**
396. *31*
397. **Luton Town**
398. **Nottingham Forest, Manchester United and Queens Park Rangers**
399. **Glasgow Rangers**
400. **West Ham United**

TED MACDOUGALL

401. *1947*
402. **West Ham United**
403. **John Bond**
404. *51*
405. **Scotland**
406. **Aston Villa**
407. **Centre forward**

408.   23
409.   Manchester United
410.   Burnley

HONOURS

411.	FA Youth Cup winners	1983
412.	Division One champions	2004
413.	FA Cup semi-finalists	1992
414.	Division Two champions	1986
415.	League Cup winners	1962
416.	League Cup runners-up	1973
417.	Division Two champions	1972
418.	League Cup winners	1985
419.	Division Three (South) champions	1934
420.	League Cup runners-up	1975

MARTIN PETERS

421.   44
422.   London
423.   Manchester United
424.   John Bond
425.   Tottenham Hotspur
426.   Nottingham Forest and Portsmouth
427.   Tony Powell
428.   Duncan Forbes
429.   Geoff Hurst
430.   Sheffield United

SQUAD NUMBERS - 2006/2007

431.	Robert Earnshaw	10
432.	Dion Dublin	9
433.	Adam Drury	3
434.	Andy Hughes	17
435.	Darren Huckerby	6
436.	Gary Doherty	27
437.	Dickson Etuhu	20
438.	Paul McVeigh	18
439.	Matthieu Louis-Jean	2

| 440. | Jurgen Colin | 24 |

1988/1989

441.	Dave Stringer
442.	Mark Bowen and Robert Fleck
443.	Malcolm Allen
444.	4th
445.	Robert Fleck (2) and Robert Rosario
446.	Robert Fleck
447.	Ian Culverhouse and Dale Gordon
448.	West Ham United
449.	Mick Phelan
450.	Andy Townsend

MICK CHANNON

451.	1948
452.	16
453.	3-2 to Norwich
454.	Manchester City
455.	21
456.	Preston North End, Aldershot, Notts County
457.	Centre forward
458.	Ken Brown
459.	Cardiff City
460.	Portsmouth

ADAM DRURY

461.	1978
462.	2-1 to Norwich
463.	Player of the Season
464.	Peterborough United
465.	Stoke City
466.	Defender
467.	Nigel Worthington
468.	Middlesbrough
469.	3
470.	He was captain

WHERE DID THEY COME FROM? - 1

471.	Leon McKenzie	Peterborough United
472.	Simon Charlton	Bolton Wanderers
473.	Phil Mulryne	Manchester United
474.	Gary Holt	Kilmarnock
475.	Mike Sheron	Manchester City
476.	Jimmy Neighbour	Tottenham Hotspur
477.	John Ryan	Luton Town
478.	Tony Powell	Bournemouth
479.	Colin Suggett	West Bromwich Albion
480.	Roger Gibbins	Oxford United

1993/1994

481. Rob Newman and Chris Sutton (2)
482. Efan Ekoku
483. John Polston
484. Ian Culverhouse
485. Oldham Athletic
486. 12th
487. Manchester United
488. Chris Sutton
489. Southampton
490. John Deehan

GARY DOHERTY

491. 1980
492. Nigel Worthington
493. Tottenham Hotspur
494. Republic of Ireland
495. 27
496. Manchester United
497. Luton Town
498. Newcastle United
499. Player of the Season
500. Craig Fleming and Damien Francis

MALKY MACKAY

501. 1972

502. Sheffield United
503. Celtic
504. Centre back
505. Sunderland
506. Bruce Rioch
507. Darren Huckerby
508. Sheffield Wednesday
509. Denmark
510. West Ham United

ROBERT GREEN

511. 1980
512. Andy Marshall
513. Ipswich Town
514. Goalkeeper
515. David James
516. 0-0 (v. Ipswich Town)
517. Sven-Göran Eriksson
518. Bruce Rioch
519. 1
520. Scott Carson

TOP LEAGUE SCORERS IN A SEASON

521. 1971/1972   Ken Foggo
522. 1976/1977   Viv Busby
523. 1981/1982   Keith Bertschin
524. 1983/1984   John Deehan
525. 1986/1987   Kevin Drinkell
526. 1991/1992   Robert Fleck
527. 1993/1994   Chris Sutton
528. 1996/1997   Darren Eadie
529. 1998/1999   Iwan Roberts
530. 2000/2001   Iwan Roberts

NORWICH V. WEST HAM UNITED

531. Kevin Drinkell, Dale Gordon, Mark Bowen and Robert Rosario
532. Mark Robins
533. Steve Bruce

534. Robert Fleck
535. 1984 (December)
536. Dale Gordon and Andy Townsend
537. Tottenham Hotspur
538. Mark Bowen
539. Ted MacDougall
540. Martin Peters

CRAIG BELLAMY
541. 1979
542. Crystal Palace
543. 32
544. Mike Walker
545. Wales
546. Coventry City
547. Jamaica
548. 13
549. Queens Park Rangers
550. Liverpool

NORWICH IN THE FA CUP
551. Notts County
552. Luton Town
553. Terry Allcock
554. Roy McCrohan, Jimmy Hill, Bunny Larkin and Bill Punton
555. Sutton United
556. Darren Beckford
557. Birmingham City
558. Southampton
559. Rob Newman and Chris Sutton
560. Terry Allcock

NATIONALITIES
561. Joe Royle   English
562. David Williams   Welsh
563. Martin Peters   English
564. John Devine   Irish
565. Youssef Safri   Moroccan

566.	Andy Townsend	Irish
567.	Bryan Gunn	Scottish
568.	Efan Ekoku	Nigerian
569.	David Phillips	Welsh
570.	Matthieu Louis-Jean	French

DAVE WATSON

571. Liverpool
572. Ipswich Town
573. Liverpool
574. He was captain
575. Preston North End
576. 1982/1983
577. 11
578. Everton
579. 6
580. Central defender

ROBERT EARNSHAW

581. 1981
582. West Bromwich
583. Nigel Worthington
584. Ipswich Town
585. Wales
586. Germany
587. Cardiff City
588. Brighton
589. Cardiff City
590. 3-2 to Norwich

1990s

591. Rob Newman, Jeremy Goss, Chris Sutton and John Polston
592. Oldham Athletic
593. Mark Bowen and Ian Culverhouse
594. Chelsea (lost 2-0)
595. Arsenal, Chelsea and Everton
596. Craig Bellamy
597. 9th

598. Mark Walton
599. Neil Adams (13) and Darren Eadie (17)
600. Craig Bellamy

CRAIG FLEMING
601. 1971
602. West Bromwich Albion
603. Wolverhampton Wanderers
604. Oldham Athletic
605. Mike Walker
606. Huddersfield Town
607. 5
608. Halifax Town
609. Calum Davenport
610. Newcastle United

EFAN EKOKU
611. Manchester
612. 1993
613. Mike Walker
614. Nigerian
615. Kevin Campbell
616. Centre forward
617. Chelsea
618. 15
619. Wimbledon
620. Sheffield Wednesday

POT LUCK - 2
621. Dion Dublin
622. Ralph Hunt
623. White
624. Newmarket Road and The Nest
625. "On The Ball, City"
626. Preston North End (H)
627. 1973 and 1975
628. West Ham United
629. Willie Reid

630.   1971/1972 and 1985/1986

IAN CULVERHOUSE

631.   1964
632.   Preston North End
633.   Everton
634.   Tottenham Hotspur
635.   1
636.   1990/1991
637.   Division 2 Championship
638.   Simod Cup
639.   Swindon Town
640.   Play in every league game

LEAGUE GOALSCORERS - 1

641.	Ken Burditt	58
642.	Ade Akinbiyi	3
643.	Neil Adams	25
644.	Les Eyre	58
645.	Jimmy Hill	55
646.	Noel Kinsey	57
647.	Duncan Forbes	10
648.	John Deehan	62
649.	Dale Gordon	31
650.	Gary Brooke	2

IWAN ROBERTS

651.   1968
652.   Welsh
653.   Wolverhampton Wanderers
654.   Barnet
655.   Wolverhampton Wanderers
656.   5
657.   Stockport County
658.   1999/2000
659.   Ipswich Town
660.   15

NORWICH V. LIVERPOOL

661. David Phillips
662. Colin Woodthorpe
663. Colin Suggett and Martin Peters
664. Terry Allcock
665. Jeremy Goss
666. 0-0
667. Jan Molby
668. 1977 (January)
669. Tom Docherty
670. 2-0

DARREN EADIE

671. 1975
672. Huddersfield
673. Andy Johnson and Keith O'Neill
674. 1996/1997
675. 17
676. Mike Walker
677. Sunderland, Watford and Portsmouth
678. 35
679. Leicester City
680. £3 million

NEIL ADAMS

681. Stoke
682. 1994
683. Luton Town
684. 25
685. Darren Eadie
686. Everton
687. 13
688. Oldham Athletic
689. Oxford and Wolves
690. Swindon Town

KEVIN KEELAN

691. India

692. 673
693. Goalkeeper
694. Wrexham
695. Ipswich Town
696. England XI
697. Norwich 'Player of the Season'
698. Liverpool
699. Cardiff City
700. Tampa Bay Rowdies

BIG WINS

701.	Torquay United, League Cup 2nd round (Sept 1995)	6-1
702.	Huddersfield Town, Division 1 (Mar 1998)	5-0
703.	Watford, Division 1 (Apr 1984)	6-1
704.	Stockport County, Division 1 (Feb 2001)	4-0
705.	Millwall, Division 2 (Dec 1985)	6-1
706.	Birmingham City, Division 1 (Sept 1982)	5-1
707.	Sutton United, FA Cup 4th round (Jan 1989)	8-0
708.	Aston Villa, Division 1 (Aug 1975)	5-3
709.	Everton, premier league (Sept 1993)	5-1
710.	Arsenal, premier league (Aug 1982)	4-2

ALAN BLACK

711. 1943
712. Lol Morgan
713. Gordon Bolland and Terry Anderson
714. Birmingham City
715. 1
716. Sunderland
717. 11th
718. Defender (left back)
719. Douglas
720. 1973

LEAGUE APPEARANCES - 2

721.	Kevin Keelan	571
722.	Bryan Gunn	390
723.	Darren Eadie	153 (15)

724.	Ron Ashman	592
725.	Justin Fashanu	84 (6)
726.	Dave Stringer	417 (2)
727.	Sandy Kennon	213
728.	Joe Hannah	398
729.	Willie Donachie	11
730.	Norman Wharton	101

MICK PHELAN
731. 1962
732. Oldham Athletic
733. Norwich won all 3 matches he scored in
734. Burnley
735. Ken Brown
736. Steve Bruce, Wayne Biggins and Dale Gordon
737. 9
738. Queens Park Rangers
739. Gary Megson
740. Manchester United

RON SAUNDERS
741. 1932
742. Centre forward
743. Oxford United
744. 1969
745. Aston Villa, Birmingham City and West Bromwich Albion
746. He led Norwich to their first Wembley appearance - the League Cup final
747. Portsmouth
748. 21
749. John Bond
750. 1973

WHERE DID THEY COME FROM? - 2
751.	Darren Huckerby	Manchester City
752.	Terry Anderson	Arsenal
753.	Colin Sullivan	Plymouth Argyle
754.	Mathias Svensson	Charlton Athletic

755.	Jurgen Colin	PSV Eidhoven
756.	Duncan Forbes	Colchester United
757.	Keith Robson	Cardiff City
758.	Carl Bradshaw	Sheffield United
759.	Phil Hoadley	Leyton Orient
760.	Andy Linighan	Oldham Athletic

MANAGERS

761.	Mike Walker	1996-1998
762.	Bruce Rioch	1998-2000
763.	Martin O'Neill	1995
764.	Ron Ashman	1962-1966
765.	Mike Walker	1992-1994
766.	Dave Stringer	1987-1992
767.	John Deehan	1994-1995
768.	Gary Megson	1995-1996
769.	Ken Brown	1980-1987
770.	Ron Saunders	1969-1973

NIGEL WORTHINGTON

771.	1961
772.	Defender (full back)
773.	94
774.	Northern Irish
775.	Doug Livermore and Steve Foley
776.	Sheffield Wednesday
777.	66
778.	2006
779.	Darren Huckerby and Peter Crouch
780.	Dean Ashton

GARY HOLT

781.	1973
782.	Kilmarnock
783.	Grimsby Town
784.	Scottish
785.	Midfield
786.	2001/2002

787. Nottingham Forest
788. 11
789. Jim Brennan
790. 5-0 to Norwich

NORWICH IN THE LEAGUE CUP
791. 5-3 to Norwich
792. Chelsea
793. Rochdale
794. Terry Allcock
795. Tottenham Hotspur
796. Darel Russell, Gaetano Giallanza (2) and Iwan Roberts (2)
797. Duncan Forbes
798. Tottenham Hotspur
799. Mick Channon
800. Halifax Town

POT LUCK - 3
801. Albert Sturgess
802. Johnny Gavin
803. 1933/1934
804. Lee Croft
805. Oldham Athletic
806. Archie Macaulay
807. Darren Huckerby, Lee Croft and Robert Earnshaw
808. Joe Royle
809. Arsenal
810. Jon Newsome

BRUCE RIOCH
811. 1947
812. Scottish
813. 1998
814. Luton Town
815. Arsenal
816. Bryan Hamilton
817. Odense BK
818. 24

819.   *Torquay United*
820.   *2000*

MIKE WALKER

821.   *Goalkeeper*
822.   *3rd in the Premier League*
823.   *Arsenal*
824.   *1992*
825.   *Welsh*
826.   *Everton*
827.   *1963*
828.   *1986*
829.   *Ian Walker*
830.   *1998*

LEAGUE GOALSCORERS - 2

831.	*John Deehan*	*62*
832.	*Johnny Gavin*	*122*
833.	*Ted MacDougall*	*51*
834.	*Chris Sutton*	*35*
835.	*Terry Allcock*	*106*
836.	*Tony Cottee*	*1*
837.	*Ralph Hunt*	*67*
838.	*Martin Peters*	*44*
839.	*Robert Fleck*	*56*
840.	*Craig Bellamy*	*32*

CAPS FOR MY COUNTRY

841.	*Chris Woods*	*43 England caps*
842.	*Nigel Worthington*	*66 Northern Ireland caps*
843.	*Martin Peters*	*67 England caps*
844.	*Joe Royle*	*6 England caps*
845.	*Bryan Gunn*	*6 Scottish caps*
846.	*Chris Sutton*	*1 England cap*
847.	*Mark Bowen*	*35 Welsh caps*
848.	*Robert Fleck*	*4 Scottish caps*
849.	*Iwan Roberts*	*15 Welsh caps*
850.	*Martin O'Neill*	*64 Northern Ireland caps*

PAUL HAYLOCK
851. 1963
852. Birmingham City
853. 3
854. Everton
855. 1981
856. Right back
857. The League Cup
858. Gillingham
859. English
860. Gary Rowell

NORWICH V. MANCHESTER UNITED
861. Ruel Fox and Chris Sutton
862. 1986 (December, 1-0)
863. Robert Fleck
864. 2-0 to Norwich
865. Mick Phelan
866. 0
867. Colin Suggett and Kevin Reeves
868. 4-1 to Norwich
869. Norwich (4th) (Manchester United [11th])
870. 1974 (September)

1994/1995
871. West Ham United
872. Queens Park Rangers
873. West Ham United and Liverpool
874. 3-0 to Norwich City
875. Ashley Ward
876. Bryan Gunn, Andy Marshall and Simon Tracey
877. Leicester City, Ipswich Town and Crystal Palace
878. Ashley Ward (2) and Jamie Cureton
879. Jon Newsome
880. Blackburn Rovers

NORWICH V. SPURS
881. 0-0

882. *Mark Bowen and David Phillips*
883. *2-1 to Norwich*
884. *Chris Sutton (2) and Efan Ekoku*
885. *Justin Fashanu and Martin Peters*
886. *David Cross*
887. *Andy Linighan, Robert Fleck and Robert Rosario*
888. *Martin O'Neill*
889. *Lower (15th)*
890. *Ralph Coates*

KEN BROWN
891. *The League Cup (The Milk Cup)*
892. *John Bond*
893. *West Ham United*
894. *Northern Ireland*
895. *1980*
896. *London*
897. *Plymouth Argyle*
898. *FA Cup*
899. *John Bond*
900. *Dave Stringer*

KEVIN BOND
901. *1957*
902. *Leicester City*
903. *Central defender (or full-back)*
904. *Norwich 'Player of the Season'*
905. *Coventry City and Leeds United*
906. *12*
907. *Leeds United*
908. *Alan Ball*
909. *John*
910. *Tottenham Hotspur*

1960s
911. *Ron Davies*
912. *Jackie Bell and Terry Allcock*
913. *Ipswich Town*

914. Birmingham City
915. Kevin Keelan and Peter Vasper
916. Terry Allcock
917. Higher (13th) (Ipswich [15th])
918. Laurie Sheffield
919. Jim Oliver
920. Ron Ashman

DARREN HUCKERBY
921. 1976
922. Nigel Worthington
923. Lincoln City
924. English
925. Robert Earnshaw (2), Carl Robinson and Lee Croft
926. 6
927. 2004/2005
928. Manchester City
929. Luton Town
930. Peter Crouch and Iwan Roberts

PAUL McVEIGH
931. Belfast
932. Wolves
933. 2000
934. Northern Irish
935. Manchester United
936. West Ham United
937. Crewe Alexandra
938. Francis
939. Centre forward
940. 18

NORWICH V. SOUTHAMTON
941. Mark Robins
942. Colin Suggett and Ian Mellor
943. 3-1 to Norwich
944. 1-0 to Norwich
945. Steve Bruce, David Williams, Kevin Drinkell and Dale Gordon

946. Ralph Hunt and Johnny Gavin
947. John Deehan
948. Rob Newman and Chris Sutton
949. Alistair Miller
950. Higher (12th)

MATT JACKSON
951. 1971
952. Everton
953. 1987/1998
954. Queens Park Rangers
955. Portsmouth and Port Vale
956. Craig Fleming
957. Swindon Town
958. Queens Park Rangers
959. Second season (1997/1998)
960. Wigan Athletic

DARYL SUTCH
961. 1971
962. Sunderland
963. Manchester United
964. Bradford City, Grimsby Town and West Bromwich Albion
965. Middlesbrough and Aston Villa
966. 15
967. 9
968. Jon Newsome
969. Nottingham Forest and Blackburn Rovers
970. Southend United

JUSTIN FASHANU
971. 1961
972. Centre forward
973. 5
974. Liverpool
975. Stoke City
976. Everton
977. Nottingham Forest

978. 19
979. 35
980. Mark Barham, Peter Mendham and Keith Bertschin

1980s
981. Millwall
982. Arsenal
983. 12
984. Mick McGuire, Martin O'Neill and Dave Watson
985. 25
986. Screen Sport Super Cup
987. 3rd
988. Watford
989. Paul Haylock and Chris Woods
990. Ross Jack and John Deehan

NORWICH V. CHELSEA
991. Jamie Cureton and Ashley Ward
992. 3-0 to Norwich
993. Steve Bruce and Asa Hartford
994. David Phillips and Mark Robins
995. Lower (14th)
996. David Cross
997. Fog
998. Jimmy Hill
999. Chris Sutton
1000. 1-0 (3-0 on aggregate)

THE NORWICH CITY FOOTBALL CLUB HISTORICAL TRUST

CONTACT DETAILS:

Address:
Carrow Road
Norwich
NR1 1JE

Telephone:
(01603) 218701

Fax:
(01603) 613886

E-mail:
historicaltrust@ncfc-canaries.co.uk

REVIEWS

"This quiz book will occupy the minds of anyone on a long trip and will thoroughly test Canaries fans, both young and old, on their knowledge of the past happenings at the club." - **Keith Webb**

"A book that every Canaries fan will not be able to put down." - **Kit Carson**

"An excellent companion on those long away trips, whilst sitting in yet another traffic jam on the M25."- **Richard Bland, Norwich City Football Club Historical Trust (Chairman)**

"A must for all Canaries, young and old. A superb range of questions that is sure to stump even the most ardent of Norwich City fans." - **www.pinkun.com**

"Chris Cowlin has delved into the history of Norwich City Football Club, to produce a magnificent questionnaire regarding the Club, its players and managers, which will leave even the most ardent and knowledgeable City supporter scratching their head. - **www.forces2canaries.co.uk**

"Whether you want to test your knowledge or learn about the Canaries, The Official Norwich City Football Club Quiz Book is all you'll need. The 1,000 questions have even tested our most knowledgable contributors, and even sometimes been surprised by some of the facts and figures. - **www.thenest-ncfc.co.uk**

"Another great addition to the quiz book series. Including questions about the club history, the players, the managers and of course our favourites: the East Anglia Derby questions. A must for the true Norwich fan."
- **www.footballderbies.com**

"Reckon you're a Canaries fan? Would you know a Gunn from a Goss? Let's be havin' you! with 'The Official Norwich City Football Club Quiz Book'..."
- **www.4thegame.com**

REVIEWS

*"This quiz book has it all, facts, figures and information about Norwich City." - **Spencer Prior***

*"Essential for all Norwich City fans!" - **Mel Machin***

*"The variety of questions ensures that both young and old can enjoy the Norwich City experience, past and present." - **Asa Hartford***

*"Amaze your mates with your knowledge of Norwich City Football Club!" - **Willie Donachie***

*"Full of facts, figures and history of a great club... Norwich City! I thoroughly enjoyed it all!" - **Peter Grant***

*"A book that every Norwich City fan will not be able to put down - an addictive read!" - **Phil Chapple***

*"All Norwich fans will enjoy this!" - **Alan Wood***

*"A must for all Norwich City fans! A true test for any fan." - **David Williams***

*"If you thought you knew everything about the Canaries, think again. This book is a factfest for all true Norwich City fans." - **John Benson***

*"A must for all Canaries from all generations." - **Joe Corrigan***

*"Great book for the ardent Canaries fan!" - **Paul Franklin***

*"A wonderful set of questions - perfect for any Canaries fans." - **Gordon Bennett***

*"A superb set of questions to test the knowledge of all canary fans, young and old." - **Adam Drury***

REVIEWS

"Just about the only thing this doesn't tell you is how many blades of grass there are on the Carrow Road pitch. Perhaps that should be question number 1001..." - Kevin Piper, Anglia Television

"Live from Norwich - it's the quiz of the century. The ultimate anorakopedia of Norwich City Football Club. Answers to questions you always wanted to ask, but felt you'd be tarred and feathered with canaries. Now, you can be Captain Canary ... the quiz master ... the font of all wisdom ... with teeth. There's enough trivia here to while away the miles on those long away trips ... It's Carrow to the marrow ... Colney to the boney ... Knowing this book, knowing Norwich. Ah hah." - Shaun Peel, BBC Look East

"This has got to be the book all Norwich City fans will want to test out their knowledge on the best team in the Country. Well done Chris Cowlin."
- Roy Waller, BBC Radio Norfolk

"Yet another cracking quiz book in this series that will delight all Canaries' fans." - Derek Davis, East Anglian Daily Times

"I really enjoyed The Official Norwich City Football Club Quiz Book. It will test the memory of every Canaries fan!" - Delia Smith

"A great set of questions for any Canaries fan to try and tackle - I was certainly caught out on a few, this book will be great for down the pub and amongst friends - a must for any Norwich fan!" - Chris Llewellyn

"A true test for any Norwich City fan, with so many questions this is sure to keep you entertained for hours!" - Neil Adams

"This book has so much information in that teaches you a lot about the history of Norwich City – I am sure you will have a lot of fun with this!" - Steve Walford